Tradin' Tales

Stories from a Montana Back Porch

Dedicated to my Sweetie.

Dawn

The Prettiest Girl in Montana ...
... and for over 40 years ...

The bride of the world's luckiest cowboy.

Tradin' Tales

Stories from a Montana Back Porch

by

Ken Overcast

BVP

Bear Valley Press

Ken Overcast is available to royally entertain you at your gatherings or special events.
Real Music and Real Stories from the Real West.

Cover Painting
H. Steven Oiestad

Rear Cover Photo
Judy Stegmeier

Illustrated by
Ben Crane

Chapter Heading Photo
Roy Matheson & Honky Tom
Chinook, Montana 1904
Charles E. Morris

Library of Congress Control Number: 2007904195

Printed in Canada
First Edition
First Printing
ISBN-13: 978-0-9718481-2-2
ISBN-10: 0-97818481-2-2

Bear Valley Press
PO Box 1542
Chinook, Montana 59523
406-357-3824

www.kenovercast.com

"There are two theories when it comes to arguing with a woman. Neither one of them works."
Will Rogers

Photographic Credits

Table of Contents

Table of Contents

Table of Contents

Introduction

*W*elcome to T*radin' Tales, Stories From a Montana Back Porch*. Steve Oiestad captured Stuart McCalmont and me visitin' on our back porch one evening and painted the picture on the cover. Stuart is gen-u-ine cowboy.... plumb to the bone, and the only difference between his stories and mine are that mine are all 100% the truth (well.... almost.)

I hope you enjoy your ride through the Real West. Although a lot of things have changed dramatically out here in the last hundred years or so, it might surprise you to find out that some of them continue essentially unchanged. A man's word is still his bond, a good saddle horse is still a cowboy's best friend, and swappin' stories remains one of our favorite pastimes.

I must concede that if a vote were taken among the cowboys I know, liein' to each other would come in a very distant second to cowgirls, as vocational diversion of choice, but it's still fairly high on the list.

Some of the most incredible of these stories are completely the truth, a few are absolute BS, and all of the others fall somewhere in the large grey area between the first two. Most of those were actually true when they happened, but for some reason seem to get better every time they're told.

Thanks for ridin' along. Enjoy.

ken

Chapter One

Lobo Number 243

It was chilly the morning that Elmer Snivley showed up for his first day of work high in the mountains near Yellowstone Park. He was fresh out of computer school, and this was his very first job. Elmer had just been hired by the U.S. Government's <u>Predator Operations Oversight & Protection Service</u> (**POOPS** for short), and his official position was "Introduced Predator Electronic Tracking Coordinator."

He would be the first one to tell you that he didn't know anything about predators, especially the wolves that had recently been reintroduced into that area from their normal range in northern Canada, but just last May he had graduated at the top of his class with a Master's Degree in Computer Science and Technology, and a Doctorate in Applied Satellite Communications. The FBI had quickly approved the required security clearance, and he was ready to go to work at POOPS' top-secret facility high in the Montana Rockies. His superior, Sergeant Loofawitz, met him at the door.

"Welcome to the Rock, Snivley," Loofawitz growled as he disarmed the security system on the double cast iron doors. "I'll show you around." After a quick tour of the command and control room and the satellite uplink station it was at long last, time for Elmer to get his first glance at a few of the animals he would be tracking.

"The entire Rocky Mountain Eco-System is depending on you ... DON'T SCREW UP!!"

"That's Old 243," said Loofawitz, gesturing towards a huge gray timber wolf lying close to the fence. The unflinching animal's keen deep-set eyes followed their every move. "They are secured here in this five-acre predator reintroduction pen. He and those two females over there came from way up by Yellow Knife." The two officers moved slowly around the outside of the fence, as the Sergeant continued. "We're in hopes that he'll mate with them, and we'll have the start of a brand new pack. They've been in here almost a month, and are scheduled to be rotated out of here this afternoon. We'll open the gate to their pen around dark, and they'll find their way back out into nature where they belong."

"I dang shore don't belong in nature anywhere around this dump," thought Old 243 to himself, overhearing their conversation, "and if they think for one minute I'd lower myself to mate with one of those ugly #@$%& (wolf cuss word) they're nuts. Their old man couldn't even catch a crippled caribou. And speakin' of caribou, I'm sick to death of this dang buffalo meat. Go ahead and open that gate, pardner. I'll ditch those too old bags and be back in Yellow Knife by next weekend."

Of course the two control officers had no idea that even though they hadn't spoken in Canadian, 243 understood every word they said, and was at this very moment planning his escape. In preparation, he'd even taken on an extra feed of that dumb buffalo meat he hated so badly ... but then, "A wolf's gotta do what a wolf's gotta do."

Back at the control room, Sergeant Loofawitz explained that each of the reintroduced predators was fitted with a satellite transmission GPS collar.

"All you have to do is watch this computer monitor. The lights on the screen each represent a different animal. By selecting the various light indicators, it will give you the predator's exact latitude and longitude. As long as the light keeps moving, everything is OK, but if one of them stops it indicates that we have a problem. If the light happens to stop inside our designated release area, don't worry about it, but if a predator ventures outside of our selected area, and it stops for more than three hours anywhere ... we've got big trouble. It will more than likely mean that one of those trigger-happy cowboys are up to their old tricks again." Loofawitz muttered something under his breath, and went on. "A stop of three hours and one minute outside of the designated area will activate this flashing light, and an alarm buzzer will sound," he said pointing to the ceiling. "If that happens pick up this red phone immediately. It is linked directly to security."

"Which security?" inquired the new recruit.

"That is information dispensed only on a need to know basis," Loofawitz snapped. "Believe me, it's adequate." The Sergeant checked his side arm then headed for the door. "There will be a guard outside at all times. Adequate provisions and a shower can be found in the back room. I'll be back in two weeks. You are not to leave your post under any circumstances. Good luck, Snivley. The entire Rocky Mountain ecosystem is in your hands. Don't let us down ... we're counting on you." Loofawitz moved slowly through the heavy double cast iron doors and Elmer heard the click as the two-week time lock was activated.

The recruit made himself at home and kept a close eye on the monitor. He was intently watching later that day, as he saw 243 and the two females make their way out of the newly opened gate.

"Sayonara, USA," Ol' 243 growled as he bounded into freedom. "You girls are on your own ... I'm outta here." He headed north down the coulee taking full ten-foot strides. He was thankful he'd kept in shape running the outside circle of the fence. "Yellow Knife here I come."

Snivley watched in horror as he saw 243's indicator light head towards the edge and continue quickly on north out of the control area. "Just my luck ... my first day on the job, and we have an escape!" His eyes never left the screen, as he began to plot 243's progress on the large map in the control room.

By daylight El Lobo had blown past Livingston and was skirting the west edge of the Crazy Mountains. He was glad he'd eaten that extra buffalo meat, even though he hated the dang stuff, and just the thought of a good caribou hind quarter made him travel all the faster. By nightfall of the first night, 243 stopped to catch his breath and take a long cool drink from the rippling Smith River. At this rate, he'd make the Missouri by daybreak.

Meanwhile back at the POOPS command center, nestled in its secret location high in the Rockies, Snivley was a nervous wreck. He was afraid to eat or sleep, keeping a constant eye on the monitor.

Everything for the new escapee went pretty much according to his plan for the first two days, but the buffalo meat was beginning to wear off, and his belly started growlin'. He was going to have to find something to eat. He topped a little rise about daylight of the third morning and layin' there in front of him was a whole field full of Limousine cows. It was the closest thing to caribou 243 had seen since Yellow Knife, so he just helped himself to a big fat one. Little did he know the fatal mistake he'd just made. They belonged to "Bugger" Maxfield, the best shot in Toole County.

He didn't feel a thing. Bugger drilled him with the very first round, and it wasn't until he got up to the carcass that he saw what he had. "Holy Cow!" Maxfield exclaimed. He knew it was just a matter of a couple of hours until the ATF the FBI the CIA, and goodness knows who else would be swarmin' all over the place.

It was a sure thing that the Feds would view this as capital murder ... plain and simple. If they could find a tree they'd prob'ly hang him right on the spot. Now, Bugger Maxfield ain't no dummy. He cut the collar off Old 243, threw it into a passing railroad car, and then gave El Lobo a proper burial, remembering the famous three S's of the West ... shoot, shovel, and shut up.

All this time Snivley hasn't taken his eyes off the computer screen. He'd gone through nearly a case of those little stomach acid pills he found in the back room, and was plumb wore out ... just snatchin' the occasional tiny catnap. The two weeks drug slowly by. Then one morning he heard the nearly silent click of the security lock and the creak of the double cast iron doors as they opened. There was Sergeant Loofawitz lurking in the doorway.

"We've had an escape, Sir!" Snivley blurted out.

"Escape?!?!"

"Yes, Sir. It's 243. But don't worry, Sir," the recruit continued, pointing towards the large map bristling with red pins on the control room table. "The longest he's ever been stopped has been just under two hours. I had no idea these animals had such an enormous range ... he's been between Chicago and Seattle four times in the last two weeks."

Chapter Two

Amorous Archie

The Old Donnelly place finally sold sometime last spring. The old folks passed on a couple of years ago, and all the kids had moved out of state right after they got out of school. None of them seemed to have any interest in the ranch ... except to cash it out and blow the money.

Dick and Billy tried to buy it, but the price that ground brings nowadays, you have to be rich before you start, and that hasn't ever been a real problem around their place. It lays right next door, too.... right up in the foothills on the south side of their summer field. It sure is a good piece of grass. The alkali flat that those guys grub out a livin' on ends just on this side of the line fence.

"Dang it, Billy. That would have made a real outfit out of this place," Dick remarked one mornin' at breakfast.

"Yup," Billy burped as he popped the top on another of his usual breakfast fare.

"Those dang pin-headed bankers are so short sighted. If those boneheads will give a feller a loan, it's a lead pipe cinch that he don't need it."

"Yup." (Billy doesn't say much when he's in the middle of breakfast.)

"Three million dollars can't be that durn much ... we'da prob'ly got it paid back sometime."

"Yup," answers Billy, slingin' the empty can across the room into the thirty-gallon barrel by the door. "Wonder when we'll get to meet the lady that bought the place? Someone said that she's some kind of kinfolk to Mrs. Sullivan down the road ... real rich, is what I heard ... from back east someplace. I guess she ain't never been married. Wonder what she looks like?"

"Real rich and ain't married?" Dick enquired. "How old is she, did you hear?"

"Nope. But Tommy Brown said he saw her, and she dang shore ain't much to look at ... but then how ugly can a woman with a three million dollar ranch be? Maybe you oughta get a handful of sweet peas and put on a clean shirt an' spark her a little."

"A rich woman with no man don't make much sense to me ... must be somethin' wrong with 'er ... prob'ly crazy 'er somethin'." Dick replied pulling on his hat. I'll go down and feed the heifers, while you water Archie."

"OK," belched Billy, as he pulled on his boots and popped the top on another barley sandwich.

Archie was the red roan stallion the boys had picked up a year or so ago at a horse sale in Wyoming. They kept him in a box stall in their ramshackle old barn,

18

and led him down to the creek for water a couple of times a day. He was a big raw boned, Roman nosed old plug and certainly wasn't the best lookin' cayuse you ever saw. He was getting a little long in the tooth too, but the trader they had gotten him from had convinced them they were gettin' a whale of a deal.

Dick had already finished with the heifer chores, and was headed down towards the barn just as Billy stumbled out of the door with Archie in tow.

"By George, there comes our new neighbor now," observed Dick. "She must be cuttin' across our place to visit the Sullivans."

Billy looked up to see Miss Vanderhoof cantering towards them on her fancy jumping mare she had brought along with her from Massachusetts. She was riding a little English saddle, and was all decked out in her hunting coat and cap with a pair of those high classed, balloon-topped ridin' britches. She sat a horse very well with a near perfect dressage posture. While the boys were crane-in' their necks to get a little better look at their new rich female neighbor, Archie had already seen as much as he needed to.

"WOW!" thought the love-starved roan cayuse as he jerked loose from Billy's half-hearted grip. He let out a squeal, rolled back his upper lip proudly showing what big yellow teeth he had left, and charged at a dead run towards the approaching mare. "Get a load of those long legs ... this sweety musta come from a chorus line in Las Vegas!! ... and that skimpy little saddle!!! ... I'll bet she had to order that from Victoria's Secret!!"

Miss Vanderhoof was a little on the naïve side when it came to things like Archie's romantic intentions, and although she was probably incapable of comprehending the base thoughts running through his rapidly approaching mind … it wasn't long until it became very apparent to her that all was not well in Camelot. Her bay mare squealed and kicked poor ol' Archie in the chest with both feet … an act of rejection that would have certainly discouraged a less motivated suitor. Not Archie.

The bay mare didn't seem in the least
inclined to compromise her convictions.

Dick and Billy just stood by the barn aghast, totally powerless to intervene in what appeared to be the bay maiden's probable undoing. Miss Vanderhoof was shrieking at the top of her lungs and pounding Archie's face with her riding crop as they galloped in frantic circles in front of the barn. She could see clearly down his throat as Archie's big yellow teeth snapped, and was horrified, as from the very depths of his being, the savage beast trumpeted his deafening amorous love calls. The high classed bay mare was obviously unimpressed by the entire turn of events, and indicated by the flashing of her rear hooves, that she didn't seem in the least inclined to compromise her convictions.

The outcome of the entire episode looked very grim indeed, until Dick got the bright idea to open the round corral gate and hollered at Miss Vanderhoof to ride in. She did ... with Archie in hot pursuit of the best lookin' thing he'd seen cross the alkali flat. Billy threw a loop around the roan's neck on one of the frenzied circles, and headed for the snubbin' post in the center of the pen. Poor ol' Archie's tongue was out about a foot as the rope quickly tightened around his throat. The lack of oxygen only had a very slight dampening effect on his passion, but it gave Dick sufficient time to throw the gate open and allow the two maidens to make their escape.

It's probably a good thing that the boys couldn't understand Massachusetts' swear words, as their new neighbor went over the hill towards home on a dead run with the bay mare wringin' her tail.

"I tol' ja she was prob'ly crazy."

"Well, Dick. I figger you 'n Tommy was
both right. She dang shore ain't much
to look at ... an' I think she IS crazy."

Chapter Three

One Way Trip To the Breaks

There's been quite a flap over the "Wild & Scenic" designation given to a long stretch of the Missouri River Breaks, and no matter if you come down on the "Rancher's, we've lived there for generations" side or lean towards the "Enviro's, ever'body deserves to sniff these flowers" position, there's one point where most everyone agrees ... it IS wild and scenic.

This stretch of country has probably got as rich a history as there is anywhere. Its rugged and remote geography has never been suited for the faint of heart, and because it's so easy to get "lost" down there, that wild country has always been a real magnet for those who have preferred to ride on the shady side of the law. How far back the colorful history goes is pretty difficult to say, but it's a safe bet it's probably been that way since the beginning of time.

Horse and cattle thieves, and anyone else that needed a good place to hide had a natural sanctuary there in terrain said to be so rough that "magpies would bust their wings just tryin' to fly over it." There was an old outlaw trail running right through the middle of it from north to south in the 1800's. Stolen Canadian horses were trailed through to their final destination in Wyoming, and misappropriated southern horses were then trailed back north to be sold in Canada.

With the end of the era of the buffalo, the half breed French Canadian/Indians that had previously lived off the land in this area suddenly found pickin's pretty slim, and Granville Stuart's DHS Ranch longhorn cattle seemed to taste almost as good. Logically the "white man's buffalo" were the natural substitute.

The problem of stolen horses and cattle got to epidemic proportions, and Mr. Stuart was not all that impressed. He organized more than one "Necktie Party" down into the Missouri River country from his home ranch north of the Judith Mountains in the 1880's. Some reports say that upwards of 20 or 30 suspected thieves were summarily hung. Although the lynchings didn't stop the problem totally, I'm sure the swift vigilante justice probably took a little of the fun out of stealin'.

Kid Curry and the rest of his Wild Bunch of outlaws are also known to have holed up down that way. They rode right through the middle of the breaks and on across the Mighty Mo after robbing the Great Northern Railway's west bound #3 at Wagner, Montana in 1901.

As time went on things tamed some, but not entirely. The old north/south horse thief trail was

24

later used by bootleggers during Prohibition to transport both home-made and Canadian booze as far south as the lucrative Denver speakeasy market, and "riders of the long rope" continued to ply their cow thievin' trade. Only the Good Lord knows all the secrets that country holds.

There's a story from the Prohibition era that illustrates both the toughness and resourcefulness of at least one family that made the Missouri River Breaks their home. One enterprising individual from that area was highly suspected by the authorities to be making and selling moonshine. Because both the geography and reputation of the area were so tough, his illicit booze business was booming.

One summer morning in the 1930's a US Revenue agent drove boldly into the yard. Other that a few chickens pecking around on the ground, the only other living creatures at home were a hungry lookin' dog, and an even hungrier looking kid about six or seven years old.

"Where's your Pa, Sonny?" the lawman enquired.

"T'aint here," the shy little country kid replied, peeking around the corner of the little log house.

"How 'bout your Ma? I'd sure like to visit with them a little."

"She t'aint here neither."

"You aren't here all alone are you? You know where they are?"

"Yea ... they're down the coulee at the still."

Paydirt! This is just what the lawman had been hoping ... confirmation of what he'd been suspecting for some time.

"Can you take me down there? I'd sure like to visit with them. I'll give you a dollar if you'll show me

25

where they are." The visitor took a big shiny silver dollar out of his pocket, making it ring as he flipped it into the air, catching it with the same hand.

The little boy's eyes widened and they never left that silver dollar as he cautiously slipped out from his hiding place. He'd probably never had a whole dollar of his own in his entire life.

"Sure, Mister," the skinny kid offered enthusiastically, his big eyes gaping even wider. "Give me the dollar. I'll take you down there."

"I'll give you the dollar when we get back," the shrewd visitor assured his young guide. The answer he received from that skinny young kid spoke volumes about life in the Wild and Scenic Missouri River country.

"You better give me that dollar now, Mister. If you go down that coulee, you ain't comin' back."

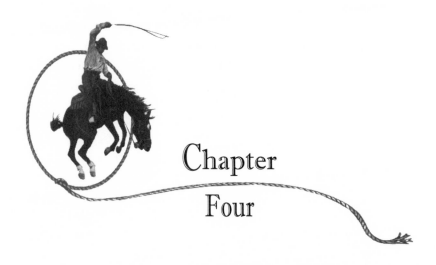

Chapter Four

Cowgirls Gotta Be Tough

I wouldn't trade this country life for a million bucks. It sure is sad to see our little rural communities slipping, the businesses having a hard time making it, and the families involved in agriculture just giving up.

There's a quote from an old time rancher, caught (like all the rest of us) in the financial squeeze of the 80's, that I will remember until the day I die. It was just nip and tuck whether he'd be able to hang on to his sizable ranching operation. His bankers were breathin' down his neck, and things looked pretty bleak. His never quit attitude exemplifies what it takes to make it through when times get really tough.

"We may not make 'er, but I ain't givin' up. There'll be slivers in my fingers when they drag me off the porch." Apparently things worked out ... they still live there, and have expanded a few more times in the years since.

We all need a little more of that attitude. There's a whole lot more to life than money. There are benefits to country living that just never show up on any balance sheet. Let me tell you about just one of them.

I'm getting a real bang out of a couple of little cowgirls that are determined to make good hands, and fortunately for me, both of them think the sun only comes up in the morning because their Grandad says it can. Being a Dad is tough duty. It's doggone hard to balance scratching out a livin' with way too little money and far too much work, with being a real Father to your children. A lot of Dads don't really think too much about that until their kids are already grown and it's too late ... almost. The Good Lord in his wisdom gives a lot of us a second chance with grandkids.

Faith Halingstad & Rio Dawn Overcast
On Ol' Benny

Rio Dawn is six years old and Faith is seven. They're cousins, and are really a couple of dandies. They both live close enough to ol' Grandad that all three of us have taken on the project of makin' cowgirls out of them. Sure, it would be a whole lot easier and faster to just saddle my own horse and ride out by myself and do what needs doing ... but then, that's the mistake I made far too many times the last time I had young'ns around here. That's just out of the question.

It's been a real kick to watch them go from being timid little sissies to full fledged cowgirls. When we first started this project they were scared of their own shadows, and lately they've taken to telling me how it's supposed to be done. Of course it's my duty to toughen them up enough so they can make useful citizens out in the big bad world someday, so I'm always chiding them with things like, "Oh, buck up. If you're gonna be a cowgirl you gotta be tough."

I'm not really sure that their Mothers appreciate everything the girls are learning out here. Rio Dawn lives in town, and her Mama (town raised) is an immaculate housekeeper and dresser. That little girl has always looked like she just stepped out of a band box. Every hair was in place, and her well coordinated wardrobe with matching shoes was always perfectly neat and tidy. Until ... she joined the gang down by the barn.

They're too short to saddle their own horses yet, but they watch very carefully to make certain that I do it just right, and are always very quick to point out what needs to be done next. Then there is always the "Don't forget the toilet paper and sunscreen" issue. Traveling with little girls does require a little preparatory adjustment. There are just a few feminine needs that MUST be taken into consideration.

I've been having the time of my life, and now that I think it all over, wouldn't trade where I live and what I've been doing for ten million bucks. I think I've accomplished my goal of making cowgirls out of those two gals, even though their manners seemed to have suffered a little in the process. The girls may think I'm just it, but I'm not too sure their Mother's are all that impressed with some of the changes they see in their little darlin's.

A couple of weeks ago we took a big ride out to check some cattle. It was quite a circle, and both the gals made it without a whimper. As I was loading their horses back in the trailer (carefully following their instructions), and telling them what a good job they'd done and how tough they were, my two little helpers were sitting cross legged on the ground, spittin' on the grass. They were attempting to share an apple, but because neither one of them has any front teeth the poor old apple looked like it had just fallen out of a cement mixer.

They were a real sight for sore eyes. Both of them were as dirty as a couple of little pigs with hair stringing out in all directions and faces so filthy it looked like they'd been nursing on an old sow. From the off hand comment one of them made, their transformation from sissies to genuine ladies of the range must be nearly complete.

"Yea ... an' we don't even have to chew with our mouth closed ... 'cause we're cowgirls."

I think their Mama's are gonna kill me.

Chapter Five

Smokey's Remote Control

Smokey Campbell sat restlessly in the waiting room, mindlessly staring at the battered old hat he was slowly turning between his knees. His wife Patty was in with a special team of doctors, and it seemed to him that they'd been in there WAY too long. He was afraid it was her heart. She had been acting unusually tired the last few days, and when she stumbled on the back steps and lost her balance and fell, it was time to check things out. He hauled her right into town.

"Dr. Lamricelli is the best in the world, the kindly old nurse at the front desk had assured him. He's a specialist's specialist. They just don't come any better than him. He got tired of the hustle and bustle of the big hospitals back east, and wanted a slower paced life, so he moved out here just last month. I've even heard he's the one they call to examine the President of the United States. Don't worry. Patty's in VERY good hands."

"That's easy for you to say," Smokey thought to himself, feeling only slightly better. "That's my little Patty they've got in there."

The time just seemed to drag. Finally after what seemed like hours, a well-dressed man in a dark blue business suit approached him.

"Dr. Lamricelli?" Smokey asked hesitantly, his eyes filled with concern and the next obvious question. He didn't even need to ask.

"No, I'm not Dr. Lamricelli, Mr. Campbell. My name is Special Agent Monroe. Don't worry, your wife is fine ... she's still in with the Doctor. Would you follow me please? I'd like to visit with you for a moment. Smokey followed down a long hallway and into a small room. The door clicked behind him. Inside were two other men that were also introduced as special agents.

"What's goin' on here? Where's my Patty?" Smokey demanded. "I want to see the Doctor!" Just then another door opened and a distinguished looking tall man in his late fifties entered, a stethoscope dangling from around his neck.

Mr. Campbell, my name is Dr. Lamricelli. Patty is fine. There's absolutely nothing wrong with her heart. I'm positive that her problems these last few days are just fatigue related. She's passed every test with flying colors. It's just a case of working too hard."

"Whew" ... Smokey was relieved.

It turns out that the special agents were helping the Doctor coordinate a high priority experiment that carried the very highest of security classifications; TOP SECRET.

"Your wife Patty is sedated and resting comfortably," the Doc assured him, "and you'll be able to see her in just a few minutes, but first let me explain why these federal agents are here. I assume you've met them?"

Smokey assured him that was the case.

"We need your help Mr. Campbell ... the United States of America needs your help."

The doctor went on to explain that although the sensitive nature of their project wouldn't allow him to reveal all of the details, here was the bottom line: The National Security Administration, in cooperation with several other federal agencies were engaged in an ongoing experimental project that involved the implantation of a very sensitive electronic device within a human body, and that Patty Campbell was a medically perfect recipient.

"You ain't gonna use my Patty fer no guinea pig!" was Smokey's original reaction. That's almost certainly the exact response most of us would have had under similar circumstances, but the doctor went on to explain to him that there was absolutely NO medical risk to his wife, and that the data they would be able to collect from this would be of great benefit to all of mankind and the United States of America in particular. He went on to explain the device further.

"Just think about it like a pacemaker for your heart ... only with a remote control. That's really over simplified, because this Electronic Feminine Behavioral Modifier is actually designed to allow remote manipulation of EVERY aspect of the recipient's behavior."

The doctor went on to give further details. There needed to be a very minor incision made in Patty's chest to implant this device, and it was imperative that she didn't know what was taking place. "Patty is the perfect recipient. First, because this is Top Secret, we need a healthy recipient that THINKS she might need a pacemaker ... that's what we'll tell her, and you must do the same. Her knowing would possibly skew the data. Also, perhaps of even more importance is the fact that we have done an extensive background investigation, and you have passed with flying colors. The Campbell's are exactly what this country needs."

Although Smokey still had reservations, further assurances from the Doctor at last convinced him that there were no negative risks to Patty's health, and he signed the necessary consent forms. Three short hours later, they were headed back out to the ranch, with the Feminine Remote Controller safely concealed in Smokey's vest pocket.

The next few days were interesting to say the least. Anytime Patty got upset about something, all Smokey had to do was sneak around the corner, pull out his remote control and push the "MELLOW" button. The time the yearlin's got out and Patty was trying to head them off, he just pushed the "FASTER" button, and she beat them to that open gate just as easy as you please.

There was also a button marked "AMOROUS". The details on the results of that button are a little sketchy, but the rumor is that the paint was all worn off of that one when the Feds confiscated the remote. You see, although things were going fine for a while, Patty sort of caught on after a few days, and it messed everything up.

Not wanting her to find the secret remote control, Smokey had to constantly keep changing pockets. Last Wednesday right after dinner, he'd slipped it into his back pocket and apparently had forgotten it was there. He'd sat down in his old easy chair, and fallen asleep. Unfortunately, the way the authorities have pieced together the sketchy information, it appears that he must have been sitting directly on the "FASTER" button. There's a clear trail leading to the south side of the ranch and a big hole in the fence. Nobody's seen Patty since.

I have contacted the necessary Federal Authorities, and volunteered our services. I assured them that "FASTER" is one control that isn't needed around here, but the other two sure might come in handy.

"Now, I don't know about you ...
but I ain't sure I believe all that."

Gabby

My pal Gabby talks too much
But ... he come by it fair
See, his Mother was a woman
An' his Dad an auctioneer

Chapter
Six

Cat-Ass-Terfy

*B*illy flipped over the hotcakes and set a couple of plates on the table. He'd drawn the short straw so his pardner Dick had spent the night nurse-maidin' their calving heifers and it was up to him to rustle up breakfast.

"Come 'n git 'er," he growled in typical camp cook fashion, "a'fore I throw 'er out."

Dick sat up on the edge of his bunk and stuffed his feet down through the pant legs that were still stuck in the tops of his boots. He was a firm believer that a fella has to learn to make ever' move count. When he stood up, he pulled up his jeans with one hand, grabbed his hat off the bed post with the other and stumbled bleary eyed in the direction of the table, his spurs lazily jinglin' on the pine floor.

He'd had a long tough night, and his eyes were still nearly stuck shut, so he didn't even see Ol' Beauregard all stretched out in the middle of the floor. Beauregard was a big stray tom cat that Billy had taken up with after he'd wandered into their camp a couple of months before. Dick never did like that dang cat, and he was just about to like him a lot less.

Beauregard was one big cat. He must have been crossed up with a Bobcat or something, and poor old Dick went head over heals into the table when he tripped over him.

"I swear I'm gonna kill that #$%& cat of yours!" Dick vowed, picking himself up off the floor. "What 'n the heck is he doin' in the house anyway?"

"Eatin' mice, ya durn fool. You mus' be plumb blind not to be able to see a cat that size. Ain't his fault you don't look where you're goin'."

One thing was for sure ... Dick was completely awake now, but the morning's bumpy start hadn't done much to improve his attitude.

"You 'member to put ever'thing in these hotcakes?" he grumbled. "I tasted Ford hubcaps that wasn't this tough."

Billy just ignored him. Normally insulting the camp cook would get the job handed to YOU, but in this case cookin' was probably easier than watching the heifers all night.

"I got my colt saddled," Billy changed the subject as cheerfully as he could. "I'll ride through the pairs down by the creek while you do the chores around the barn.

"Yea ... all right ... &^%$ cat," Dick snarled, glaring at Beauregard, who was indignantly returning his stare.

The boys finished their breakfast then cleaned up the mess and headed for the barn. Like a shot, Beauregard was the first one out the door, hitting the crack at a dead run, nearly tripping Dick again.

"I hate that &*$# cat!"

"Ah lighten up. You know dang well he's a good mouser," Billy stuck up for his feline friend.

Dick headed for the corral to throw a little hay up for a couple of cows, while Billy bridled his colt and led him out of the barn. The boys met at the door, and Dick slid it shut as he went inside. Billy was slowly circling the horse in the yard in front of the barn to limber him up a little before he stepped on.

Cats are nasty. They understand a whole lot more than we give them credit for. Beauregard knew Dick hated him, and the feelings were mutual. Soooo ... just to get even for the cussin' he got for simply minding his own business and taking a nap in the middle of the kitchen floor, Beauregard figured that sharpening his three inch claws on Dick's new saddle was perfectly legitimate.

Dick wasn't impressed. With a string of words that would make a sailor blush he took after that huge cat with a scoop shovel vowing to send him directly to pussy cat heaven. Beauregard hit the stairs up into the barn loft at a gallop with Dick right on his heals, wildly swinging the scoop shovel over his head.

Meanwhile ... out in front of the barn Billy has just stepped up on the big sorrel four year old colt he's breakin'. The colt hasn't offered to buck, although there is quite a hump in his back. Billy is busy stroking his mane and trying to talk him out of it, far too preoccupied to notice the chaotic catastrophe occurring just behind the door.

When Beauregard clears the top step and realizes that he's still got a deranged cowboy with a scoop shovel hot on his tail, he takes a split second to analyze his options and realizes that (unfortunately) he's cornered. The only other way out of the hay loft is the open door at the end of the barn. The fifteen foot drop to the ground doesn't look as attractive at the moment as standin' his ground and fightin'.

"Besides, I never liked that *&$%# (cat cuss words) Dick anyway," he snarled to himself as he spun around in the center of the loft and bared his teeth to face his charging foe.

"You want a piece o' me ... jus' come an' git 'er!'"

Dick definitely missed his calling. The Calgary Flames could use a boy that can wield a hockey stick like he did that scoop shovel. He fearlessly caught the twenty pound Beauregard with the back of his shovel in a near perfect shot and catapulted him out the open door with one whack.

Dick still recalls with fondness the sight of that cat silhouetted in the early morning light as he flew with legs outstretched through the doorway of the barn loft. Beauregard was not having a good morning ... and he was just about to mess up Billy's. Cats always seem to land feet down for some reason, and this landing was stacking up to be perfect ... almost.

With his claws outstretched as far as they'd go, Beauregard made a perfect four pointer right in the middle of the sorrel colt's rump. The momentum of the falling twenty pounds of catapulted cat, the freshly sharpened claws, and the soft meat of the horse's rear end were a disastrous combination. The poor cayuse had no idea what he'd done to deserve such treatment, and immediately decided to unload everything; Billy, Beauregard, saddle and all.

Dick had a free ringside seat from the barn loft. Billy's creative "double back flip" dismount was the first thing he'd seen that made him smile all morning. He still claims that Beauregard put up a lot better ride than Billy did.

No one has seen ol' Beauregard since. It's probably just as well. He'd pretty well worn out his welcome anyway. The gravel in the yard really didn't do Billy a lot of good either.

"That $#%* cat!" he snarled as he wiped himself up out of the rocks.

"Ah lighten up," Dick cackled, echoing his pardner's words as he helped him to his feet, "you know dang well he's a good mouser."

41

"But, why should I have to top 'im off fer ya, Billy??

Yer the one that just fell off.

An' all cuz of yer dad-blamed cat!"

Chapter
Seven

Winter.... A Real Pain In the Rear

*T*he last REAL rough winters we've had around here were in the late seventies. We had a couple of pretty bad ones in a row back then, with lots of snow and cold weather. Jack Gist is a salty old timer that lives down the road a ways from here, and he's been predictin' that we're going to have another one of those "good old fashioned winters" like that again.

Of course, he's been predicting that for about twenty years now. So far it hasn't happened, but being the unflappable old sage that he is, his lack of accuracy up to this point doesn't seem to bother him a bit. "I've lived in this country a long time, and I know that if I just keep on predictin' a tough one ... she's gonna come true one of these times, you just wait 'n see." You know, I think he's probably right.

We had a little TD6 with a dozer on it, and couldn't get the road open in '77. We just had to sit tight until a guy with a bigger machine got it unplugged. That sets the stage for this little TRUE tale. It was the winter of '77-78 and the whole country was snowed in.

I'm going to change the names of the stars of this little show ... for two reasons. First off, being the sensitive guy I am, I'd like to save them the obvious embarrassment; and secondly, knowing them like I do, I feel a deep inner need to prevent any potential physical damage that may inadvertently befall my neck as a result of me spillin' the beans after all these years. This deal is still a real sore spot ... literally.

Eight or ten of the neighbors had gathered over at Bob's place. A couple of them had gotten there in their chained-up four wheel drives, a few more on snow machines, and I think a couple of them even had to come on horse back. You see, Bob had a big four wheel drive tractor with one of those wide dozer blades, and the neighbors had all gathered to help him dig the blade out of the snow bank and get it mounted on the tractor so he could plow them all out.

This really wasn't that big 'o deal. The boys located the dozer blade right away and got it drug into the shop where the tractor was parked. Bob had a nice new shop building, with a propane heater blowing warm air so everyone was in out of the cold. They drug the blade around where it needed to be, and a couple of guys started screwin' in the bolts.

"Holy cow it's cold outside," Jack shivered as he backed up to where the air from the heater would blow on his frozen hands.

44

"Check out the bottom drawer on the far end of the workbench," Bob called from under the tractor. "There might be a little antifreeze left down there."

There, squirreled away safe from prying eyes, the boys found Bob's private stash, a fifth of Canada's finest. Two guys workin' and ten guys standin' around is not a safe place for a bottle of hooch when it's cold outside. On perhaps the bottle's third or fourth round, one of the boys spied an old Winchester 22 leaning in the corner.

"Whatcha been shootin'?" came the logical inquiry.

"The doggone sparrows like to hang out in here for some reason. I've been knockin' 'em out of the rafters in here."

"How do you keep from shootin' the place full o' holes?" Tom questioned.

Bob climbed back out from under the tractor, wiping his hands and grinnin'. "Ah, it's just got birdshot in it. Heck, I don't know how it even kills a bird. Watch this," he continued as he grabbed the old Winchester and let's 'er fly at the wall, barely twenty feet away.

There was hardly a mark on the sheetrock, on the far wall. "See, I tol' ya," Bob grinned as he took his first nip from the now not so full bottle.

The boys stood around visitin' in the warm shop, plinking at the sparrows in the rafters and finishing off Bob's stash. They say there's a direct correlation between the unbridled and indiscriminate ingestion of Bob's anti-freeze, and lack of intelligent decisions made by its ingest-ees. It must be true.

"Yer right, Bob," Tom hiccupped, that birdshot don't even put a mark on the sheetrock, how in the dickens does it kill a sparrow?"

45

"I dunno," Bob slurred in return. (He had been desperately trying to catch up with the neighbors and get his share of his stash ... successfully, I might add.) "Go down to the other end of the shop, an' I'll shoot ya in the butt and show ya ... it won't even go through yer Carhartts."

"Oh, no you don't ... YOU go down to the other end of the shop and I'll shoot YOU in the butt."

"OK ... I will." Down to the far end of the shop he went, to the great joy of a very appreciative audience. (Alcohol has been proven to kill brain cells. Bob must have lost several that afternoon.) "Make sure you hit me in the rear end though," Bob cautioned, raising his hands over his head to avoid any stray buckshot.

"Don' worry ... I'll hit-cha all right," Tom assured his idiot friend as he took careful aim at the rear end of Bob's Carhartts, fully 60 feet away.

There are some basic laws of physics that the boys failed to take into consideration; the main one being the difference in the density of Carhartts and sheetrock. The rifle cracked. Bull's-eye!!

Bob let out a squeal like a turpentined monkey, and began shedding his clothes. I've never really put much stock in all of that evolution stuff, but in this particular case, I'm not too sure that maybe Mr. Darwin might just be on to something. This sure looks like "missing link" behavior to me.

Bob spent the evening on his belly on the kitchen table, with his exposed tail section directly under the light, and his dear little wife dutifully picking out the buckshot. Rumor has it that she didn't have a lot of sympathy for the stupidity of his predicament, so

46

was not as gentle as perhaps she could have been. After the removal of eight or ten BBs they gave up (probably by mutual consent) agreeing to meet back at the table right after breakfast.

Our hero stood up for breakfast that morning, and an early morning perusal of his south-side revealed that the wound had sealed over, and any further attempts at surgery would be futile.

For years after that, those old iron tractor seats would chaff Bob's behind, and ever' so often a blister would form back there, someplace around the corner where he couldn't see, and another piece of shot would fester to the surface.

Nobody really knows if they're all out of there yet or not. There's just no way of knowin'. There IS one thing I do know for sure, and Bob would be the first one to agree with me ... tough winters can be a real pain in the rear.

"And they've got the nerve
to call US dumb animals!"

"Doggone it, Billy ...
What in the dickens do you s'pose would possess
a feller to just stand there an' get shot?
You even got more sense 'n that!"

Chapter Eight

The Preacher & His Colt

I sure like history. My grandkids think I ARE history, and I guess maybe they're right. For a long time I had the mistaken idea that great historical things only happened in other parts of the country, but I've come to realize that we're all living right in the middle of it.

I had the opportunity to spend a lot of Sunday mornin's as a kid in the old Methodist Church here in Chinook with a picture of the founder, "Brother Van", hanging on the wall. It still hangs there as far as I know.

He was a circuit ridin' preacher that came up the Missouri River to Fort Benton on a steamboat in the early 1870's. Now there's an old boy with some history. The name his Ma had given him was William Wesley Van Orsdel, but that was way too long and dignified sounding for Montana Territory, so he was just known as Brother Van.

It seems he had a natural knack when it came to gaining friends, and could relate to folks from every station in life. Charlie Russell was a pal of his and even painted a picture of him hunting buffalo with the Blackfeet ... they were his friends, too.

In fact, Charlie and a couple of his old cowboy compadres attended revival meetings back in the late 90's, in the old church that Brother Van started here in Chinook. One of the cowboys went on to become one heck of a preacher.

Charlie didn't seem to "get religion" at that particular meetin', and although he had a great respect for the Good Book and those who preached it, it just might have been his affection for booze that stood in his way. It's no secret that Charlie liked a little nip or two on occasion, and with the Temperance Movement going great guns about that period of time, he may have thought that keeping a safe distance from any real commitment might be a more comfortable position.

Carrie Nation was headed around the country about then with a hatchet; choppin' up saloons and bustin' up those kinds of places with a vengeance. She was a formidable force, standing nearly six feet tall in her sockin' feet. I think she met with a fair amount of success, too ... that is until she ran into May Maloney down in Butte. May was an Irish lady with a substantial build of her own, and as fate would have it, was proprietress of a saloon/dancehall combination along with her boarding house for single girls.

It seems that the boarding house girls specialized in short term romance, and neither they nor Madam Maloney looked too kindly on an old lady with a hatchet upsetting their little apple cart. The lady proprietor, in true sporting house fashion, drug the would-be hatcheteer out into the middle of Mercury Street by the hair and gave her a good Irish whuppin', after which Miss Nation promptly reboarded the train and left for parts unknown.

50

All of this fuss didn't seem to faze Brother Van. He was welcomed into many a saloon to preach while the gaming and drinking were temporarily suspended and the patrons given a generous helping of the Good News. The collection plate frequently contained everything from gold dust to poker chips, with the saloon owners always happy to redeem the chips ... often at more than face value.

The preacher also volunteered his services as a scout for General Howard as he pursued Chief Joseph and the Nez Perce after the Battle of the Big Hole in western Montana. Who better to guide the cavalry than a local who had spent several years galloping around the country on horseback?

Chief Joseph   Brother Van

With the Big Hole Battle just over the hill, it was a pretty scary time for the settlers in and around Bannack, the first capital of Montana Territory. The town was barricaded against the Indian attack they all felt was imminent. The ranchers and miners from the surrounding area flocked into the safety of town, and Brother Van, being the resourceful type, saw all of that able bodied help and promptly organized a work crew and began a church raisin'.

It sure is funny how the spiritual appetite of the most reprobate of old characters suddenly improves when death is staring them in the face. I played a few tunes in that old building not too many years ago. The dreaded Indian attack never came, but that old church house still stands to this day.

He was a real church planter, having started over a hundred congregations across our fair state. Of course, as things grew he needed more and more help. On one particular occasion he had in his company a zealous young preacher from back East. The young man was preparing to take over a recently constructed church in Belt, Montana, and was being introduced around the community. Brother Van noticed the Catholic Priest coming down the street in his buggy, and was anxious for this young associate to meet his old friend.

After a few pleasantries, the young man, being young and zealous, made a comment to the Priest that he felt the Father's fancy driving team and buggy were a little excessive.

"But my son," the old priest explained, "my Parish is very large, and I have many miles to travel in a short amount of time."

"The Lord Jesus made due with the colt of an ass," the young man sharply retorted.

"I can't seem to find one ... although I've searched high and low," the portly old friar answered slyly, winking over his glasses at his old friend, "... but unfortunately it appears they've all become Methodist Missionaries."

52

Chapter
Nine

Cowboy Fun

*I*t's been said that cowboys have a twisted sense of humor. It's pretty easy to get your nose out of joint when a fella calls you something as uncomplimentary as "Twisted", but I've been giving it some thought and I believe I'm beginning to see how someone totally uneducated in the finer points of "Good Clean Fun" could arrive at that conclusion.

The rub comes with the difference in outlook. First, I know this is probably going to break a few female hearts, but I really need to point out that cowboys are NOT actually bullet proof. It's just the fact that they THINK they are that tends to push their pranks a little over the edge once in a while. Ordinary folks with just plain old normal brains have an awful hard time relating to that point of view.

Let me give you an example or two of "Good Clean Cowboy Fun." Back in the 50's or 60's sometime those fancy little bridles came into style. Before that time the headstalls on the bridles that cowboys used were fairly substantial with heavy brow bands and a nice sturdy throatlatch. For some reason, they just weren't "cool" enough for some of the fancy pants rodeo types, and the style got to be those little ear bridles ... some of them didn't even have a throat latch at all. I guess if you're just trottin' around in a rodeo arena they might be OK, but if you better not take a ride with ol' Andy.

One of Andy's favorite tricks was to ride up to a "friend" that was sportin' one of those fancy little ear bridles without a throatlatch and just pull the bridle over the ears on his pal's horse. Ideally the horse and the victim of the prank are probably both about half asleep in the middle of a ten thousand acre pasture when the "joke" takes place. The first thing the poor old horse knows, the bit and bridle hit him on his knees and Andy lays the knot end of his lariat across his rump. The (now very-awake) horse is, at least momentarily, being ridden by Andy's soon to be ex-friend.

Heaven knows what's going to happen next, and it's great fun. That is unless you happen to be the guy on a totally out of control horse galloping wildly across the prairie with his bridle off and tangled up in his front feet. I've never known of anyone actually dyin' from one of those little escapades, although I've seen a few guys get skinned up a little. Come to think of it ... maybe cowboys ARE bullet proof.

Then there's the little trick that Ed Solomon pulled on Connie Cox. Several years ago Connie went out to the Bear Paws to help the Solomon's brand. There was quite a crew of the bullet-proof types around there, so it's really hard to say just what might happen. Connie volunteered to wrangle the horses in before breakfast.

"Sure," Ed answered appreciatively. "You can ride Mom's little mare. She's tied right in the barn."

That was all the truth ... well almost. There WAS a little mare in the barn all right, and Ed WAS breaking it for his Mother, but that's about where the truth ended. She was a fancy little thing they'd gotten from Kirkaldie's out by Lodge Pole. Those folks had some mighty fine horseflesh, and a lot of them were at least partially descended from the old US Cavalry remount stock.

The Solomon outfit bought several colts from them, and Ed's Mom had picked this one out of the bunch. The fact was, she was a waspy little rascal that would buck if she got half a chance. I don't think she ever got gentle enough that Ed would let his Mother try her.

Now, Connie Cox was a champion bronc rider, so just imagine the glee felt by the entire crew when he came walkin' back to the barn after being unloaded by "Mom's little mare." He swore everyone to secrecy. Imagine the humiliation. He'd still like to keep it hush-hush, so don't tell anybody.

It couldn't have happened to a nicer guy. What goes around comes around. Not too many years later when Duane Werk's kids were getting big enough to ride, Connie dropped off a fancy little Shetland pony in their corral one day. Duane wasn't home.

"Better not ride him 'til yer Dad gets home," Connie warned the kids, "and tell Dad he better ride him first 'cause he's been turned out for quite a while."

What a set up. Duane told me he'd NEVER been bucked off that hard. I'm not too sure any kids had EVER ridden that horse before ... well, maybe out of a chute when Connie was making buckin' horse riders out of his boys. If that durn thing ever got gentle enough for the kids it was a miracle.

55

Then there's this little story a little closer to home. What's almost as fun as getting someone bucked off a knot head is making them THINK they could get in a mess when the horse is really a pussycat.

I finally got my brother John to come ridin' with me again a couple of weeks ago. He got crippled up the last time he helped me gather cattle, and has been pretty head shy ever' since. That time he broke three or four ribs and dislocated a shoulder, and had to ride all busted up that way three or four miles back to the trailer. (Well, we DID have to finish movin' the cattle.)

We had him pretty well mounted too, and he's a heck of a cowboy, but we were headin' off some yearlin's in the brush and his horse ran off into a washout. Somehow John wound up on the bottom of the pile. It crippled the horse up so bad that we had to get rid of him, but you just can't shoot your brother, so we gave him a couple of years to heal back up. His shoulder never quite back like it was before the wreck, but he seems to be able to pick his nose with the other hand OK.

"Aww come on. I need a little help," I encouraged. "We've got a horse all cut out for you."

John was justifiably skeptical. "Probably some jug head that'll run off into a washout 'er somethin'."

"Naw…. This one's OK. You can ride ol' Marvin."

"Marvin? That's a dumb name for a horse," says my chicken-livered brother as he looked side-ways at the rolled–back white eyes and the quiverin' flanks of the bay gelding.

"We just changed it … couldn't get anyone to get on him … named him after Marvin Edwards."

"Marvin Edwards … the U-U-Undertaker??"

Chapter Ten

Whupped Real Bad

J've never been much of a fighter. It's just seems to be too dad-blamed hard on my eyes. The cook around here might volunteer the fact that I ain't much of a lover either, but just to be on the safe side, let's not ask her opinion. This next little story is about a guy that THOUGHT he'd taken an awful beatin' ... and it's plumb the truth.

I've taken the liberty to jumble up a few of the facts a little so that I won't reveal the true identity of the parties involved. However, any resemblance to persons real or imaginary is purely intentional. My only hope is that I've disguised them adequately enough to keep from gettin' the dickens pounded out of me.

It was about mid morning on a warm September day as Nolan Roberts reined in ol' Wheeler in front of the little tavern. Wheeler was the old horse he'd gotten over on the Reservation. The Roberts Ranch had bought him a few years ago from Frank Wheeler, and one of the conditions of the sale was that they had to either name him "Frank" or "Wheeler". Because they already had a horse named Frank, the decision was fairly easy.

Now, nobody ever calls Nolan by his first name. He's known far and wide as "Red Nose" Roberts, and he's earned the title fair and square. Over indulgence in intoxicatin' illicit liquids is a real problem for ol' Red. To be perfectly frank, he's a drunk. That's why he has to ride ol' Wheeler the ten miles into town for a little snifter. The narrow minded Sheriff over that way has seen to it that his driver's license has been revoked.

Now, Edith is a peach of a gal. She's been married to Red for over forty years, and heaven knows she's had a rough row to hoe. I guess one of the things in the old boy's favor is that he isn't a mean drunk, and he works like the dickens when he's out on the ranch, but tryin' to keep him out of town is almost a full time job.

About mid afternoon, Edith was in town in the pickup to get a few groceries and what does she see but ol' Wheeler, tied up to a light post out in front of the Battle Creek Bar & Grill.

"Why that ol' coot! He told me he was goin' to look at the heifers … and here he is in town … again!" Red Nose Roberts was in big trouble. Edith marched right in to read him the Riot Act.

"Now, don't be gettin' yer tail in a knot, Ede," Red grinned as he patted the cook a little. "The heifers is jussshed fine. Me 'n Wheeler iz jussshed a little thirshty, that's all."

"Wheeler COULD probably use a drink, but it looks like you should be fairly well watered up by now!" Edith snapped as she surveyed Red's obviously inebriated condition and the half a dozen empty glasses on the bar. "Let's go home! I'll follow you to make sure you make it."

Wheeler whinnied to his old partner as he staggered out of the saloon and up to the light pole to untie the reins. Under Edith's watchful eye, Red somehow managed to salvage what little was left of his pride by getting into the saddle under his own power, and down the street and out of town towards home they went.

The horse knew the way back to the ranch, so the only problem was to figure out how to stay on him. Now that was a challenge. Part of the time the world would spin and ol' Wheeler's head would stay right where it belonged, and then all of a sudden without any warnin' at all, Wheeler would start spinnin, and the world would stand still. It was awful, and poor ol' Red was hangin' on for dear life.

Jack Thompson lives on the trail about four or five miles out of town, and by the time they got there, it was obvious to everyone (except probably Red) that they weren't going to make it all the way home. They pulled up in Jack's yard and Edith went in to get a cup of coffee to try and dilute the poison in the old reprobate's stomach. Red climbed down off his spinnin' horse and sat down on the ground. He and Jack were havin' a fine visit, and the coffee seemed to be helping some, when Red got an idea.

"Jussshed back the pickup down here in this lil low place, Ede. I kin jussshed load ol' Wheeler up. He's gettin' sort of tired anyhow, and it'll be a lot fashter gettin' home. I'll jussshed ride here on the tail gate an' hang on to 'im." (It's no wonder ol' Wheeler was tired ... after spinnin' down the road for four or five miles.)

Edith dutifully backed the pickup down in the little swale and Wheeler climbed right in. Red was

59

smack in the middle of telling Jack some big yarn, and was talkin' and laughing and slobberin' all over his shirt. He finally finishes his story and plops his skinny old frame down on the tailgate with the reins in his hand.

"OK, Ede. Lettttssss head 'er fer the barn. See ya, Jack. Thanksss fer the coffee. Better give 'er a liddle gash, Mama she's settin' in a lil hole."

Edith "gave her a little gash" all right. When she wound up the motor and popped the clutch, the pickup lurched to a stop, and she dumped ol' Red right out on the ground. He fell in a big limp heap, still laughin' and slobberin'. The old boy wasn't hurt, but he dang near jerked Wheeler's head off with the reins being wrapped around his hand like they were. The poor old horse was about half turned around with his nose back by his tail. He was balanced precariously on one foot, tryin' his best not to fall down.

Red got back up on the tailgate, and the horse got himself all straightened back out, but now the old soak had thought of another story, and was bendin' Jack's ear with a dandy. Poor old Edith, bless her heart, was waiting patiently. In a few minutes Red was ready to go again.

"OK, Ede. Lessshh go. But lessshhh do 'er right this time. Don' fergit to give 'er a liddle gash."

This time Edith didn't forget to give 'er enough gas. That old Chevy pickup shot out of there like a rocket. The problem was that her cargo couldn't keep up, and she left it all on the launchin' pad. Red fell out in the same sort of a heap he did the first time, but instead of the engine stalling on the pickup like it did previously, this time it kept going. The two wraps of the reins around the ejected cowboy's hand was sufficient to jerk ol' Wheeler over backwards and out of the pickup box.... right on top of the pile. The horse floundered around and got back up, but poor ol' Red was knocked out colder than a wedge.

Edith thought she'd killed him, but her neighbor assured her that he was still breathin'. Jack stood over him and began to fan him with his hat to give him a little extra air, and in a few minutes Red began to come back around.

I don't think that there's much rhyme or reason to what goes through a drunk's twisted mind, and apparently Red had the facts of his predicament just a little jumbled. The only thing his bleary red eyes could see was someone with a boot by each of his ears, fanning him with a hat, and these were the first words out of his mouth.

"Don' hit me again, Jack. Fer God's sake don' hit me again. I had 'nuff ... I had 'nuff."

I was just wondering ...

If a cat always lands on its feet ...

And toast always hits the floor butter side down ...

What happens if ...

You butter the back of a toasted cat???

Chapter Eleven

Honest Officer.....
That's Really What Happened

NOTICE: This little story is all the truth except for the part I made up. Any resemblance to real persons, places or events is purely intentional. It is to be ingested for educational purposes only, and any inadvertent entertainment value is merely the result of a very light sprinkling of BS accidentally but carefully applied by the author.

My friend Glenn is a pretty resourceful guy. He can do just about anything. Country boys just sort of come by that naturally, I think. He's got himself one of those Government deals goin' now, so he probably even gets a real paycheck with insurance and everything.

Sure beats farmin'. 'Course I think he still does a little of that once in a while, too. This agriculture stuff is sort of like takin' drugs ... once you get started it's dang hard to quit. He can drive nails and he's one of those computer whiz guys, too. I think you might just call him sort of multi-purpose.

Well ol' Glenn took on this little deal to drive the Triple T Trailer Sales truck in his spare time. He runs down to the Midwest, or wherever they get that stuff, and hauls all kinds of trailers and bale haulin' pickup beds back up this direction.

There's some sort of a law on the books that says a trucker has to take a rest once in a while. I think it must have been shoved through Congress by the Federated Truck Stop Café Cooks of America. They seem to be the ones that stand to make the most money off a law like that.

It really isn't that bad o' regulation, when you get to thinkin' about it. If a guy's been out balin' hay half the night and falls asleep in his chair after supper before he goes to bed, it really isn't a biggie. But…. if the same guy has been doublin' back hauling feeder cattle to the Midwest for about six loads in a row with no rest, and then has on a load of hogs and is right in the middle of Denver at 75 MPH when he takes a little nap, things could get a little messy. That's a good way to scatter raw pork chops and heaven knows who else all over the Interstate.

The problem is that they pay those guys by the mile. Dumb idea. Even truckers are smart enough to figure out that the more miles they drive the more money they make. That's probably why they're all so wealthy.

A better solution would be to simply pay 'em all by the hour and tell them, "Just go ahead and take your

64

time, we're in no hurry." Then there'd be no need for a law to make 'em take a nap.

Well, that's just what Glenn was doin'. He was in some truck stop down in the Midwest someplace, and had just enjoyed the usual trucker's supper: A soybean laced 'burger fried in two year old axle grease, chased down with six Rolaids, and topped off with a cup of coffee that'd wake the dead. (The Rolaids are mandatory, or the soybean/axle grease combo won't let you go to sleep.) He was right in the middle of his nap, dreaming of custom made Peterbuilts, or whatever it is that truckers dream about.

The parkin' lot had several other trucks in it with all the drivers taking their law required snooze. Well, at least most of 'em were nappin'. Bernie was in the sleeper of the red Mac that was parked right behind Glenn and a few yards up the gently sloping asphalt.

This guy Bernie was on a run from LA to New Jersey with a load of auto parts or something, and had picked himself up a passenger ... just to help keep him company and pass the many lonely miles.

Her name was Trixie, and she seemed to be a nice lady, even if she did wear a little too much makeup. It seems that she was self employed and had recently been operating her business from a street corner in LA. She was looking to relocate her operation to New York, and was in need of transportation.

Because business had been a little slow, her available fundage was insufficient to buy a ticket so she'd hitched a ride with Bernie. They say on the

Evenin' News that these low interest rates are good for small business, but somehow Trixie must have missed the boat. She also brought along her toy poodle; a little white piece of fluff named Puddles, complete with a custom made leash and a pink rhinestone collar.

It appears that Bernie and Trixie were back in the sleeper just doing what was required by Federal law and had left Puddles in charge of the truck. Bad idea.

Those little lap dogs can sure get excited sometimes, and Puddles was yappin' and galloping big circles around the cab.

On one of his rapid laps, one little fuzzy paw happened to land on the switch that was hooked to the deal that holds the brakes, and all of a sudden the Mac started downhill towards the backend of Glen's truck.

Sheriff Glen Huestis

Of course, nobody noticed but Puddles, and he was too short to see and steer at the same time. *Crash!!* ... right into the back end of Glenn's load.

The collision definitely caused a violation of the law because they were all supposed to be asleep. The now-awake drivers got out to survey the damage.

Glenn's outfit was none the worse for wear, but the Mac had her front end smashed in pretty good. As it was now morning and almost time to hit the road again, the boys exchanged company information while Trixie straightened her dress and patched up her makeup.

"Nobody's ever going to believe that durn dog caused all of this mess," Bernie complained as he took a disgusted look at Trixie, now bathed in the warm glow of the new morning sunshine. (She didn't look near as good in the daylight.) Meanwhile, Glenn was quietly writing his company contact information on the back of his business card.

"The boss ain't ever gonna believe this ... and what about the cops?? They won't believe it either ... This is like the old 'dog eatin' your homework excuse.' They ain't gonna believe that dad blamed dog is responsible for all of this," Bernie said as he looked at the company information Glenn had scratched on the card.

"Hey, what's yer name anyway?"

"It's on the back of the card."

The look on Bernie's face would have been worth a hundred bucks. He slowly turned the card over and read the back out loud.

"Glenn Huestis, Blaine County Sheriff, Chinook Montana."

"Now Billy, if they'd o' just had a dog
like ol' Lucky here, that stuff would
o' never happened. He'd either been
plumb asleep 'er else runnin' all over
the parkin' lot waterin' down all the tires
and lookin fer his own girlfriend."

Chapter Twelve

Almost a Hero Once

Everybody needs a hero or two.... someone that they admire and look up to. As a young sprout, I wanted to grow up to be just like Audie Murphy. He was the most decorated soldier in World War II; a REAL hero. A lot of folks may not know that Audie was too short to get in the Army and had to stand on his tiptoes to pass the physical.

His size may have had something to do with all the extra risks he took in battle. Maybe he was trying to prove that he really WAS big enough to get the job done... who knows? I do know that the Congressional Medal of Honor was among the huge pile of decorations on his chest when he returned from the war. Unfortunately, most of the guys that earn that particular citation never get to enjoy it ... because it's been awarded posthumously.

Little boys have a tendency to gravitate towards the tough soldier type of heroes. It's probably just a part of growing into manhood. The older I get, the more I've begun to recognize a different kind of hero. They all possess those same qualities of bravery and determination that Audie Murphy displayed on the battlefields of Europe; it's just that they've got a different type of battle to fight.

Artie Tilleman is a hero of mine. I used to enjoy doing a little day work riding years ago and was a regular around his outfit for a long time, helping them move and work their cattle and ship the calves in the fall. I got to know Artie and his family pretty well. They've got good cattle, and they'd sure feed a fella good, even though you had to get up before breakfast if you figured on keepin' up with the boss.

Artie's a big man ... inside and out, and was a great guy to work for. His Dad's name was Art too,

Artie Tilleman
One of My Heros

which is probably the only reason that a guy his size would get tagged with "Artie". He's probably as much over the average man's size as Audie Murphy was below it.

I don't think he knew his own strength. When Lester Warburton was drilling a water well for him, he commented to me that, "Artie always wants me to tighten the three-quarter inch galvanized pipes with the pipe wrench. He says he just can't tell when they're tight ... all of a sudden they just twist off."

I remember when I got the news that there was something wrong with Artie's health. I was in the café in town and ran into Floyd Flynn. Floyd was way up in his eighties by this time, and as a lot of guys that age do, talked a little loud so that he could hear what he was sayin'.

"Doggone, I heard Artie's got that dang muldi-rossis."

I'm not really sure what "muldi-rossis" is, or if that's what he's got, but it wasn't long until it became apparent that there was something wrong, and little by little the disease began to chip away at probably the biggest and strongest man in the Milk River Valley.

Artie's not a quitter. Heroes don't quit. He drove his pickup longer than he really should have, and when his legs wouldn't work well enough for him to climb up into the tractor, he'd pull himself up with his arms so he could do the summer fallowing. He finally had to give that up, too.

There are a couple of things besides Artie's will and gut-tough determination that qualify him for hero status in my book. They're his attitude and fourteen inch smile. Invariably that big grin is the first thing anyone would notice about him, and when asked how he's doing, the answer is always the same, "By golly ... pretty good."

Life isn't fair. He's been stuck in a wheelchair for years now. The last time I saw him, he was having trouble talking, but his smile was as big as ever. That's the kind of stuff a hero is made of.

I got to be a hero once ... only because I was mistaken for Artie. Never mind that he's a foot taller than I am and outweighs me by a hundred and fifty pounds. It was the winter of '78 or '79. Boy, it was cold and the snow was deep. As I headed down the road to feed some cows, I noticed Floyd Flynn (the old fella that told me of Artie's illness). His little Ford Falcon pickup was stuck in the snow about halfway across his hayfield.

"Looks like ol' Floyd's stuck," I thought to myself as I turned in his gate. We probably had eighteen inches of hard packed snow, and I wondered how in the world he'd gotten that far before getting hung up. I had a load of hay on the four wheel drive, and it was chained up all the way around, so I didn't have any problem at all chewing my way in to his bogged down little pickup.

You don't live to be as old as Floyd was by being dumb, and there he was reared back in the driver's seat reading the newspaper. To try walking for help could very easily have proven fatal for a man his age.

"You need a pull, Floyd?"

"Sure do. I figured someone would be along after while." I hooked on and got him pulled back to where the snowplow had cleared the county road.

"Thanks, Artie," he called out the window as he putted back down the road towards town. I got a good chuckle out of that one. But come to think of it, there I was, a hero ... at least for the moment ... even if it was just a case of mistaken identity.

Chapter Thirteen

The Refigerator Police

I need to tell you about one of the scrapes I had with the law. Now, I'm a law-abidin' type (for the most part). The only problem I really have is when some dumb law doesn't make any sense. I guess a fella isn't supposed to think for himself ... just do as he's told. That never was my long suit.

Before I start my story, I'll give you a dumb law "for instance". The seat belt law is one of my pet peeves. As far as I'm concerned it's about the stupidest thing anyone ever thought up. I've already got a Mama that makes sure I wash behind my ears and don't pick my nose in public. I doggoned sure don't need the government tellin' me what's good for me, too.

The powers that be tell me that wearing one will help preserve my life. Well, maybe that's so, but I've been in a few scrapes where gettin' out or off in a hurry was by far the wisest decision, so although I'm not sure I concur with their conclusion, let's just say for the sake of argument that statistic is true. I don't have a bit of a problem with encouraging folks to wear one, but passing a law to that effect is trompin' on my rights. The problem here is that it's MY life, and I think I've got brains enough to figure out what's good for me all by myself.

In my opinion, the only reason our goof-ball lawmakers pushed that one through on us was because folks who think for themselves were too busy trying to make a livin' to watch everything that comes out of the Capital.

I know ... I know ... you're thinkin' this guy is a real nut case.

"Hey, Ethyl, come and read this! I told you that Overcast guy was off his rocker!"

Well, Ethyl, he's probably right, but don't stop readin' on that account. Go ahead and hear me out anyway. After all you've probably read all the way to the end of a few other things I've written that didn't make much sense.

Here's the question: Where is the line where the laws that protect me from myself stop? It's not a question of seatbelt or no seatbelt, it's a matter of principle. Please consider this fact: According to the news reports I've read, one of the leading killers in our country is overweight. We're a nation of fatties.

Obesity kills way more folks than not wearing a seat belt. Where are our all-knowing, conscientious lawmakers when we need them? I think they're dropping the ball. Come on guys, what are you waiting for??

So ... if you follow this law makin' frenzy to its logical conclusion, the next thing they'll come up with might be Refrigerator Police. It's a fact; fat kills people... it's hard on your heart. Assuming this statistic is also true, it's apparent that our citizens don't have sense enough on their own to control their fat intake.

We're killing ourselves, and the government MUST do something about it. What is needed is legislation to aid in the protection of the public. Violators will be threatened with fines or maybe even imprisonment if they're repeat offenders.

I can hear the politicians now: "I will leave no stone unturned until this cancerous drain on our health care system is stopped. OBESITY is the primary cause of increased insurance rates! OBESITY is the cause of our hospital overcrowding and rising rates of heart disease! OBESITY is a national menace, depleting the federal treasury, and conscientious Americans of every race, creed and economic class are lining up to support my new Anti-Fat legislation.

This scourge on our society must be stopped, and I make this pledge to you today, my fellow Americans; send ME to Washington DC! I assure you I will make it my top priority! With your help we can totally eliminate fat from the United States of America!"

In a way, I think that politician is right ... this new law should probably be invoked on a Federal level (sort of like the seat belt law) where Federal aid dollars could be withheld if any rogue states failed to comply. It could possibly require a policeman beside every refrigerator in the U.S. to stop folks from sneakin' in and harming themselves. (On the other hand, with the reputation that cops have for eating donuts ... who's going to keep them out of the refrigerator?) Maybe a better way would be an alarm that's hooked up electronically to the main Office of Internal Security. After all, it is our internal security that's at risk here.

See how stupid all this nonsense is? Don't you really think what a fella eats or whether he wears a seat belt is his own durn business?

This finally leads me to the story. I swore I'd go to jail before I paid a seat belt fine. I'm a man of my convictions, (misplaced as they may be) and believe in putting my money where my mouth is. I think maybe it was Will Rogers that said, "A man that stands for nothing is bound to fall for anything."

After a little fender bender (which was the other guy's fault), the investigating officer asked me if I had on my seat belt at the time of the accident.

"No." (There were no witnesses, and I didn't have to tell him that. Intelligence wasn't ever my long suit either, but Mom told me to always tell the truth.)

"I'm sorry, but I'll have to write you a citation for that," was the officer's reply.

"Just take me to jail ... I ain't gonna pay it. That's a dumb law, and it violates my rights. This is a matter of principle." (Have I ever mentioned that even though my family tree goes sort of straight up, there fortunately isn't any evidence of drain bramage?)

"Now, don't get all excited ... it isn't that big o' deal. I don't make the laws, I just enforce them. Besides, the fine is only $20."

"I told you, I ain't payin' it! Put the cuffs on me and haul me in if you want to, but I ain't gonna pay it!"

"Now, just relax, Mr. Overcast. Maybe we can arrive at a compromise. I'll trade you."

"For what? I told you I ain't gonna pay it, and that's all there is to it!"

"Sir, your license plates are expired, and the fine for that is $45. I'll just ticket you for the seal belt violation and overlook the over-due plates. That will save you twenty-five bucks."

After mulling the situation over in my mind for about a half a second ... "I'll take it! You got yourself a trade!"

... so much for my high and mighty principles. Will Rogers would be danged ashamed of me.

76

Chapter Fourteen

Ol' Fish Hook

$\mathcal{D}$ick and Billy had rattled their old pickup over west of the big mountains to a bull sale last spring, and were pointed back towards home.

"Dang it, but it's nice out," Billy burped. His bleary eyes taking in the beautiful pine covered slopes. "Whadaya say we lay over a day 'er two and do a little fishin'." Dick was all for it, but they didn't have anything along for a fishin' trip. They'd just figured on running over to the bull sale and right back home.

"Ahh, what the heck, we just put the cows in a fresh field, an' I s'pose the rest of the stuff 'll prob'ly wait." The boys finally came to the conclusion that if they'd just stop by one of those dude ranch kind of places, that maybe they could get a little fishin' gear and some advice on the where the best spot might be to throw a line in the water.

77

"Welcome to the Triangle X" was the sign out by the highway, "Guided and Unguided Fishing Trips, Horses, Canoes and Hiking."

"Why not?" Dick asked himself as he pulled into the lane that led to some fancy looking log buildings down by a roaring little stream, "Looks like we oughta find out somethin' here."

They were met by a fancy-pants lookin' guy with a rhinestone shirt and his pants stuck in his boots. He said his name was Tumbleweed Tex, "... but most folks in these parts just call me Tex." He assured the boys that they were in the right place all right, and he could fix 'em right up.

After Tex gave his little sales pitch on the many varied and exciting activities available, the decision was made to rent a couple of horses and some fishin' gear and head up the creek into the National Forest that was butted right up against the Triangle X.

"The fishin' is good right here," Tex assured them, "but if you go four or five miles up the creek it's even better. That's what I'd do if I was you."

The fancy-pants wrangler motioned over to a couple of sorry lookin' cayuses tied to the pole fence. "You can just take Champion and King. Don't worry, they're nice and gentle, and there are a couple of poles and some fishing tackle right in the first door there in the barn. Good Luck!" he yelled over his shoulder as he put on his best bowlegged cowboy impression and strode over to another car that had recently driven in.

"Gentle ain't the word fer these sorry &%$#," Billy complained as they coaxed and prodded the two old plugs up the trail. "This sucker acts like he's been dead fer quite a while already, and the rigger-mortis has set in."

"Didn't think t' bring any spurs," Dick moaned in agreement. "Didn't figure a fella'd need spurs at a bull sale, but I shore wish I had some now. I think ol Tumbleweed was right, though. Don't believe there's much buck in 'em."

The two ol' boys finally kicked and prodded and whipped the two old nags up the trail until they got to the spot that had been described to them, and lo and behold, but ol' Tex sure hadn't steered 'em wrong. They caught a nice Rainbow Trout with almost every cast. It was the best fishin' they'd ever been in. In fact, they got to where they were just saving the big ones and throwing the little ones back. Both of 'em had their limit in nothin' flat.

The sun was starting to burn red in the western sky, and even with as much fun as they were havin', it was time to head back down the creek. They gathered their gear, tied the fish on, and started back down the narrow trail towards the dude ranch.

"Me 'n ol' Sparkplug ... I mean Champion, will take the lead," Billy grinned sloppily as he opened another can of his favorite brand of liquid refreshment. "You an' ol King can try to keep up if ya can."

Neither one of those plugs amounted to anything, but the one Billy was ridin' was by far the worst. He was so dude proof that he did what he wanted when he wanted, and there wasn't a whole lot a fella could do about it. His tail was stickin' about half way out all the time and about ever third or fourth step he'd stop right in the middle of the trail and simultaneously reach down for a mouth full of grass and break wind.

A nag like that would be a frustrating thing for a decent hand to try and ride, but both of the boys were feeling the effects of the hot sun, the lazy afternoon, and the two six packs of dinner they'd consumed, so they were just lazin' along. Billy's eyes were almost as shut as ol Champion's, and he'd completely given up on getting him to do anything. He just let the sorry old horse plod along and graze and break wind as he pleased.

About half way home, there was a sudden turn of events. Dick was bringing up the rear on the trail with his reins and the fishin' pole in one hand, and a beer can in the other one, when suddenly ol' Champion took a notion to stop, graze, and break wind as was his custom. Neither Dick nor ol' King noticed, and they ran right smack into the back of the outfit in front of them.

Dick's fishin' pole was sticking out in the front, and it slid in perfectly under that half raised tail, with the hook implanting itself firmly in a very tender portion of Champion's anatomy. That old plug took off like he was shot out of a rocket, with the reel on Dick's pole making a little whirring sound as it vainly attempted to supply the sudden demand for more line.

Champion and Billy were now both very awake and in a dead run down the trail, but the real action took place when they hit the end of the fishin' line, and the hook did what hooks are supposed to do. The line broke, and that old nag came uncorked.

Billy's a pretty good skinner, but he didn't quite get ol' Champion covered.

"That must be why they call 'im Champion," Dick mused as he rode up, eyein' his pardner sprawled out on his back, moanin' in the middle of the trail. "Dang shore got the best o' you. I think that durn Tex lied to us. I'd a swore he said that horse was broke."

For some reason, from Billy's crumpled position on the ground with a fresh horseshoe print on his back, the humor in the situation was a little more difficult to see.

It took them a couple of hours to catch the horse, and another one to tie him down to get the hook out, but all was not in vain. Here's what Tumbleweed Tex wrote in a card he sent the boys last fall:

"Thanks for fixin' Champion. When he gets to stallin' on the trail now, all we have to do is pull a little line out of a fishin' reel. That little whirrin' sound is all it takes to perk him right up. Oh ... one more thing ... we never tell the guests why, but we changed his name to Ol' Fishhook."

81

"I still can't believe it ...

Here me 'n ol' Champion was jus'
goin' down the trail an' mindin' our own
business when some joker that calls
hisself a friend sticks a fishhook in m'
pony's rear end an' then gives 'er a jerk.'"

82

Chapter Fifteen

The Corn Flakes Cure

*I*f cowboy BS'ers had a union, they'd more than likely kick me out ... that is if they'd ever let me join in the first place. I really don't think there'll probably ever be such an organization, (... because who in the world could they possibly trust to take care of the dues money?) but if such an association did actually exist, there are a couple of rules that would most definitely be in their by-laws.

1. Never, ever tell a story that's 100% the truth. (There are lots of good reasons for this one, but we won't go into that now.)
2. Never, ever tell a story that makes you look like an idiot. (The reasons for this one should be fairly obvious.)

This little story is going to break 'em both. It's not only all the truth, but it's also going to make me look sort of stupid ... (although I really don't need much help in that particular area.)

The fall of 1970 found me and my bride on a place on Clear Creek on the north side of the Bear Paw Mountains. I was working for Harry Olson, and it was sometime between Thanksgiving and Christmas. The cattle were shipped, the hay was all up, and we were doing the usual fall chores.

Harry had an old wooden grain bin with a pile of rye in it that he'd thrashed a year or two before, and he wanted to take it in to the feed plant in town to have it mixed with a little barley to be made into pellets for the cows.

Boy, was that some awful stuff. It was full of smut or ergot or whatever that stuff was, and the dust was as black as coal. Bein' the low man on the totem pole, it was my job to get in the bin and shovel that valuable commodity into a little auger that he'd stuffed in a window. I don't know if anyone has ever died from breathin' that black junk, but it sure wouldn't surprise me any if that were the case. I think it was beyond a doubt the worst bin I've ever had the pleasure of shovelin' in my life.

By the time we finally got that truck full, I was in pretty bad shape. I could hardly see, and breathin' was almost out of the question. I was coughin' and spittin' that black goo on the ground, and would have given a month's pay for a drink of water. Of course, we didn't have one.

It was late in the afternoon by the time we got the tarp on the truck and headed the seventeen miles or so into town. We dumped the truck at the feed plant, with the elevator operator wisely donning a face mask as the black dusty smut cloud enveloped a couple of blocks in both directions.

"Thirsty?" Harry asked as we got back in the truck.

Boy, was that an understatement. I would have gladly sucked the juice out of the bottom out of a hoof track at that point.

"Yea, a little," I bravely understated in return, not wanting to let on exactly how bad I felt. Cowboys are tough, you know.

We stopped in at the Bar X down at the foot of Main Street. Blondie Austad was the proprietor, and the place was running over with rancher types. Ma Blatt ran the restaurant in the back of the bar, and it was getting close to supper time, but of course we couldn't eat because the women folk were looking for us to be home. That very well may have been mistake number one.

Getting something to wet your whistle at Blondie's was fairly easy, and in retrospect I perhaps should have been a little more selective about what I ordered. In all fairness, there WAS water in that concoction someplace, but not enough to counteract whatever else was in there. That was more than likely mistake number two.

Harry likes a little nip once in a while, and not wanting to look like a slacker in front of my boss, I ordered what ever he had, and drank as many of them as he did. The exact numbers escape me, but with all the neighbors in town celebrating the Holiday season, the count would have been fairly substantial. That was definitely mistake number three. But then, cowboys are tough, you know.

It was snowing big ol' flakes as we at long last pointed the truck back south to the ranch. Whatever else was mixed in with that water I drank at Blondie's had quite a grip on me by now. I couldn't have hit a bull in the rear end with a scoop shovel. We were late for supper, but really not too bad. It was only about 7 o'clock or so.

The little bride and I were camped four or five miles up the creek from the home place where Harry lived, and when we arrived at his place, I got in the old International feedin' pickup and headed up the county road for home.

It was becoming clearer to me all the time that Blondie Austad had apparently tried to poison me. Everything seemed to happen in slow motion, and my entire body felt like it had been pumped full of Novocain and then submerged in molasses. To make matters worse, the hood ornament on the old pickup kept spinnin' around in the windshield, and the fences on either side of the county road kept crossing each other.

Cowboys are tough, you know, and I had to make 'er home, so I pulled the old pickup into four-wheel drive just in case that durn road tried to give me the slip, which it in fact did on a fairly regular basis.

By the Grace of God I made it home. They say He looks out for children and idiots, and I dang shore wasn't a kid anymore.

Even the door knob was hard to catch as I stumbled into the porch. The cook had left me a little note that she had gone to a baby shower or something and that I was on my own for supper. Something to eat didn't even sound good by now. A nice padded casket would have looked a whole lot better, but I knew that one of the keys to possible survival just might be getting something in my stomach to dilute all that poison.

Dang that Blondie anyway.

I found a box of corn flakes, and a big pitcher of milk and clumsily began the dilution/detoxification process. I started to shovel down that cereal like my life depended on it. Things didn't go very well. Upon reaching its designated destination, the milk and corn flakes immediately began a rapid assent back to the bowl from which they had come. It was not a pretty sight.

The next morning told the tale. It had stopped snowing the minute I'd gotten home, and there were four-wheel drive tracks going from one barrow pit to the other all the way back to the home ranch. Unfortunately that wasn't the worst of the tale. Apparently, there had been TWO pitchers of milk in the fridge. One from the cow we were milking, and one full of milk-replacer that the cook was feedin' to a bum calf.

Yea ... you guess it. I had picked the milk-replacer. Don't let anyone tell you that milk-replacer will mix with that tanglefoot poison that Blondie used to peddle, because it won't.

All was not lost however, because only a dang fool will refuse to benefit from his mistakes, and I have definitely learned my lesson.

I haven't touched corn flakes since.

"Milk Replacer?? Serves him right".

Girlfriend

"I had me a girlfriend once
She was a purty thing
Started talkin' 'bout a weddin' dress
An' a diamond ring
But then things sort of headed South
I had to turn her loose
Said I'd have t' take a bath
An' quit a chewin' snoose"

Chapter Sixteen

Severence Pay From the Diamond X

There's not a lot that can get under a cowboy's hide, but there are a few things that most of them would just rather not do. One of them is wranglin' dudes ... that's almost the bottom of the barrel.

Not long ago I ran into an old pardner of mine that I hadn't seen for over thirty years. I'd heard he'd been killed in a wreck when the brakes went out on a truck he was drivin'. The story I'd gotten was that he was haulin some cows off a lease in the mountains in Wyoming and had wound up down in the bottom of a canyon underneath a truck load of cows. Imagine my surprise when I ran into him down by the stockyards one day. It was even worse than I'd heard. He ain't dead at all ... he's a dude wrangler over in Jackson Hole.

That's one of the main reasons cowboys are dead against gun control. When you run onto a deal like that how can you put the poor guy out of his misery??

Naw, I didn't shoot him, but I dang shore felt sorry for him. He's totally lost all of his self respect.

Then there's another guy I need to tell you about. Dave Kilgore is a good ol' boy and has his head in the right place, at least most of the time, but he wound up fallin' into another one of those traps that cowboys try to keep their feet out of. He's gotten himself a job workin' for one of those rich absentee ranch owners from back East.

Oh, I guess you really can't blame either one of those guys with the way things are goin'. Real ranch jobs on workin' ranches are getting' harder to come by all the time, and when you do finally find a good place to work, the poor ol' rancher hasn't got any money, so you're almost as well off without any job at all.

Well ol' Dave went to work for the Diamond X. I hope I never get that poor. It belongs to a trust-funder from the east coast by the name of Abigail Vandersnoot. I guess it isn't her fault that she was born in a bed with silk sheets on it, but rich knuckleheads like her sure make it hard on the folks that are tryin' to make a livin' off this land.

Ms. Vandersnoot is in her early sixties someplace and a little portly of build. The only time she was ever in the Real West before was the jillion times she flew out to California, and then she saw it from forty thousand feet of altitude. But she's a cowgirl now, by George, although I've heard she has to special order her Wranglers with the forty eight inch waist.

The first thing she did was to hire Dave ... "because he's a real cowboy, and I want a real wild west ranch."

Yea, right.

Dave was broke and down on his luck, and the rumor has it, had been drinkin' pretty heavy for a day or two before he accepted the job. When he finally regained his mental faculties, it was too late. He'd already given his word, so he had to go through with it. Besides, a regular paycheck probably has some appeal, even when a guy's sober.

The first thing the boss did was have Dave haul most of the cows to town, because "they're making those disgusting little piles all over the grass." I guess that's not all bad. Now they have grass to burn, and the few cows that are left sure don't bother the fence much.

One of the main things that Ms. Vandersnoot found attractive about hiring Dave was that he looked the way she thought a cowboy should look. I think it was a pure accident that she actually found someone that knew what he was doing, and other than putting up with some of the old girl's Eastern stupidity, it was almost like being on a pension. He really had it pretty easy, and the "bunkhouse" was like livin' in the Ritz Hotel compared to some of the shacks he's had to camp in.

Dave had actually gotten to sort of like his new boss. She was always asking his advice about "proper cowboy protocol." Bless her blue-blooded heart, but she really wants to fit in and create a genuine western atmosphere for her eastern friends to come visit. As with a lot of folks with too much money, she doesn't care if the outfit actually functions ... it just has to LOOK right.

Well, things took a turn for the worse, and Dave got himself canned. Here's what happened:

"I had a heifer that was calvin' about bed time, and it looked like it might be an hour or two before she was ready to deliver, so I stayed up and read the paper, and went and checked her again. She still wasn't ready and needed more time, so I went back in and pulled off my clothes and climbed into bed. I dosed for a few minutes until that little automatic alarm clock in my brain went off, and after a look at the real clock, got up to check the heifer again.

It was a warm evenin' last April (in the forties someplace) so I just left on those old sweat pants I sleep in and pulled on my boots. I grabbed my hat and overall jacket by the door and headed down to the barn with the flashlight. I was pretty sure she'd have the calf by herself anyhow, and I could just go back to bed. That ain't the way things worked. It was almost two in the morning by now, and I could see the heifer was going to need a little help, so I got her caught and strung out the calf puller.

It wasn't a real hard pull, but I ran into a genuine snag. That little ratchet deal on the calf puller got all tangled up in one of those big ol' legs on my sweat pants. The calf was about half born, and I couldn't stop where I was and try to untangle the durn thing, so I didn't have much choice. The calf's tongue is hangin' out and I'm in a hurry, and I can't get the puller untangled, so I just kicked off my boots and pulled off my sweat pants and finished the job with those britches going around and around in the calf puller gears.

The calf was fine, and I stuck him in a pen with his Mom, and thought all was well ... except for those old purple sweat pants. They really got chewed up in that little ratchet deal, and were a real mess.

"The heck with them," I thought to myself. "They look like they're plumb shot anyway. I'll just dig 'em out of there in the morning."

I have to admit there was more of a cool breeze than I thought there was. I pulled my boots back on and headed back to the bunkhouse in my BVD's. In all fairness I probably WAS a sight for sore eyes all right, but just when I got under the yard light, here comes Ms. Vandersnoot out of the big house.

She's all decked out in her Holstein hide vest with those big ol' Wranglers stuffed in her boots and has on her fringy shirt with the rhinestones on it. It seems she was up listening to some of her opera music when she saw the light go on in the barn, and was comin' down to watch the action.

'David Kilgore! That is not proper attire for a cowboy! I expect authenticity on my property! Gather your belongings ... your position is terminated immediately! To avoid any wrongful discharge litigation, you may rest assured that a complete severance package will be forthcoming from the accounting department!'

"I guess she must have meant I just got fired ... and after I saved the ol' Bat's calf, too."

Severance package?? Accounting department?? As soon as I lose what little pride I have left I'm headed over to the Diamond X. I hear they're lookin' for a new hand, and I've still got a couple of those rhinestone shirts around here someplace that I used to play music in ... if they'll just go around my belly.

The Author & Jiggs

Cuttin' out Pairs Last Spring

Chapter Seventeen

Illegitimate Profit

*S*exual indiscretion has been known to get folks into real trouble. But with hormones bein' what they are I suppose that it's inevitable that it will happen on occasion, and our outfit isn't any exception.

I don't think he was really to blame. After all, she'd bat the long lashes on those big liquid eyes of hers and flash the most seductive looks his way until self control was entirely out of the question. That's not even to mention her alluring auburn hair glowing in the dim light of evening, or the enchantment he felt when the shadow of her shapely feminine form cast its spell on the hillside strewn with wild flowers, hopelessly entangling his heart.

He'd been around. Some might even say, "A man of the world." There had been many short term relationships in his jaded past, and he almost instinctively knew that he was probably not the first love in her life, but that didn't matter. All that really mattered now was the moment. He must seize this moment, and cherish it forever. Over the fence he went to properly consummate the passion he felt in his heart.

It was the best thing that ever happened around here, that's for sure. The female in this little story was a Hereford cow that belonged to our son TJ, and her impassioned lover was a Limousine bull that belonged to the neighbors. The ill-fated relationship didn't last; they seldom do. They have a way of being short term by nature, but the product of that little tryst was a heifer calf that grew into the best cow we've ever owned. In fact I don't think it would be an exaggeration to say she was the best cow in the State.

Now, I'm sure I've got ever' cowman for 500 miles in every direction mad as the dickens and just itchin' to prove that they've got the best one, so I'd better explain a few of the reasons I believe she qualifies for that designation and then let everyone make up their own minds.

We called her TJ ... much to our Son's dismay. Just imagine the humiliation of a young fella in puberty when his friends discover he has a cow named after him. Well, it WAS TJ's cow and she carried his initials on the brand on her hip, so the name stuck. When he left home to strike out on his own, we somehow traded him out of her. What ever it was that we wound up giving him for her, it probably wasn't enough. (I sure hope he doesn't read this.)

She was marked like a red-necked Hereford and weighed in at over fifteen hundred pounds when she

96

matured. The Limousine blood in her veins certainly didn't hurt her milk production, that's for sure. She was the best doggone milker on the place.

The first couple of years TJ was in production were fairly normal. She was just a regular part of the herd around here, and as a young cow, brought in a couple of nice big calves. It was the year she was four years old that she really began to prove her worth.

I don't know how other cow outfits work, but around here if there's an orphan calf or one that needs a little extra attention, the cook is the one that takes care of it. I like to think that because of her natural maternal instincts, she's just more suited for that kind of thing. She's certainly got more patience with a dummy that's too sick or dumb to suck than I do that's for sure, but if the truth were known, I don't think she'd let me do it anyway. In her opinion, I'd more than likely just screw things up.

The spring TJ was four years old, we had a bum calf that needed a Mom for some reason, and because we didn't have an extra cow, I went to the pasture and just picked up the cow with the most milk. That'd be TJ. She was a joy to work with, and wound up raising both calves.

That was the beginning of a long and profitable relationship. As a matter fact, she was so easy to put extra calves on that it became a regular practice around here to pull calves from old or sick cows and just give them to TJ in the spring. There was only one more year (the summer that she was 17 and was so old that we felt sorry for her) that she only raised her own calf. She always had at least two and many times three or four.

She did have one itty-bitty strange quirk. My tiny little cook could go out into a pasture and put her hand on the old girl's hip and she'd stand perfectly still for a little orphan to nurse, but she didn't like getting milked. That was a no-no.

"Yea, right," says I, the undaunted hero of ranch womanhood. "You mean to tell me you can't get me a bottle of milk from that gentle old cow?"

"Nope, she doesn't like to be milked. She kicks like a Government mule."

Not being one to take no for an answer, I proceeded to show the little woman the proper method and technique for milking a gentle nurse cow. I hate to admit it, but she DIDN'T like to be milked. She stood about fifteen hands high, and calmly placed one of her five foot long hind legs up by her ear and then let it fly in the opposite direction, sending me across the calvin' shed on my keester. She had a real Jekyll & Hyde personality, that cow.

TJ's crowning accomplishment came the summer she was 18 years old. For some reason we wound up with more than our normal run of bum calves and she miraculously acquired three additional ones as well as her own. It was supposed to be a temporary situation, but that's not how things worked out. She nursed all four of them that summer with no extra feed at all.

Our steer calves weighed about 650 pounds that fall and three of her calves fit right into the bunch with the little one that didn't make the cut weighing about 500 or so. I sure wish I'd have gotten a picture of that.

If her record doesn't qualify her for *The World's Most Profitable Cow Award*, then I don't know what it would take. Please consider these facts:

1. She had a calf every spring for seventeen consecutive years.
2. She raised more than one calf every year for fourteen of those years.
3. It's our best estimation that she weaned at least 40 head of calves. With a conservative weaning weight of 550 pounds, that places her production at approximately 22,000 pounds of beef at weaning time.

She turned twenty this spring, and I guess all good things must end. She ran into a few problems and her baby didn't make it full term. We turned her out by herself and we reluctantly rounded her up and hauled her into the sale barn in August. It was like losing a member of the family. But even in her departure she made us proud. Twenty years old, she weighed 1450 pounds and grossed $754.00.

Not a bad end for the illegitimate by-product of an illicit relationship. Who said that foolin' around doesn't pay?

"So ... tell me,

Just what was the reward for the world's
most profitable cow?? A one way ticket to
Ronald McDonald's, that's what!

You talk about injustice.
I think we need to unionize."

Chapter Eighteen

Bear-ly Scared

*I*t had been a good fall, the cattle were all shipped and the cows were in a fresh field with lots of grass, so Dick and Billy got the urge to go elk huntin'.

"How 'bout we load up our horses and some groceries and head up to the Bob Marshall Wilderness?" Dick hiccupped as he finished off his breakfast. (A barley sandwich.)

"That's a heck of a good idea," Billy belched in reply. "We can take along our fishin' poles, too. You gather up some grub, an' I'll run in the horses. I'm sick o' fixin' fence anyway."

In a couple of hours the two ramshackle cowboys were rattlin' their way towards the mighty Rocky Mountains with their pickup box loaded down with gear and a trailer load of horses draggin' behind. Now, Dick was a pretty experienced hunter and had been in the "Bob" lots of times in his younger days, but the only wild game experience Billy ever had was with the barmaid down at the Stockman.

"Ain't there bears up there?" Billy asked his pardner, trying not to sound too scared.

"Yea!" Dick grinned with a gleam in his eye. We might just get one o' them too!"

"All we got is a couple of elk licenses," Billy stumbled. "We better not mess with no bears."

"Now, how in the dickens is a bear gonna know if 'n we got a license 'er not?" Dick grinned again as he shifted the old pickup down to pull a hill.

They got to the jump off point at the trailhead into the wilderness just as the sun was going down, and made camp there. The next morning they were off shortly before daylight, riding a couple of their best mounts and leading three packhorses all loaded up with their gear. Billy was a little spooked about bein' in bear country, although he didn't want to let on (Cowboys are tough, you know.) But he finally confessed.

"I never did like bears too much," he remarked as bravely as he could, looking over his shoulder. "What 'r you figgerin' on doin' with one if you get 'im?"

"Heck, we'll just camp out up here 'til we eat him up. Nuthin' like a good bear steak."

They were two days packin' in on the trail and pitched their camp in a big meadow beside a little stream that was running over with trout. It was just like bein' in paradise. The next morning found them up at daylight again, in earnest search of the elk they were sure they'd find.

Oh, they found them alright, but didn't have much luck. Billy shot up all of his shells in the first half a day and couldn't hit a thing. Dick didn't have any luck either, but had only gotten off a shot or two.

Their guns were different sizes, so poor ol' Billy was just up the creek.

"I told you to bring more shells."

"I was gonna, but there wouldn't have been enough room for the beer."

That seemed like a reasonable argument, and Billy was enjoying the ride and the scenery anyway.

Along about two o'clock in the afternoon on the way back to camp, what should they jump but a big black bear. Dick didn't have time for a shot as the old bruin loped down a slope and into his den in the rocks, with the boys in hot pursuit. Well, to be honest the boys really weren't in agreement about just how fun this was. Dick was in hot pursuit, but Billy was taggin' along at a fairly safe distance.

When they got up to the den, they had a problem. They knew he was in there, but it was too dark in the hole to get a decent shot. Dick leveled his rifle at the door of the cave, but Mr. Bruin was too smart for that. They could hear him in there, but he wouldn't come back out.

After a few minutes of waiting, it was time for another plan.

"Go throw a rock in there, Billy," Dick ordered, still peering down his gun barrel.

"Not me! I don't like bears, remember!"

"Dang it, Billy! This might be our only shot ... 'sides he ain't a grizzly. It's just a little black bear. You ain't scared are you?"

Cowboys are tough, you know, and that's one of the best ways to get 'em to do something really dumb. The very suggestion of being afraid was all the encouragement that Billy needed. He tied his horse a little ways away and picked up a hand full of rocks and began chucking them into the door of the cave. There was a lot of growlin' coming from in there, and Billy was scared to death, but he was way too proud to admit it.

"That ain't workin', Billy! Get yourself a stick, and poke him in the face. When he comes out I'll nail him!"

"I never DID like bears," Billy thought to himself as he reluctantly headed to the bear's den with a long tree limb. *"How in the dickens did I get myself in this mess anyway?"*

This time it worked. Out charged old Bruin with his teeth a snappin' and Billy in his sights. Dick was true to his word, and got a shot off right away. He was sure he'd hit him good and hard, but the bear had turned around and headed back into his den. Billy didn't have a clue if he'd hit him or not. He had his back turned to any place a bear might be and was takin' forty foot strides down the mountain. He didn't stop running for at least a hundred yards.

"Got 'im!" Dick crowed to Billy as his shaky kneed pardner finally gained the courage to climb back up the hill. " ... but he crawled back in his hole to die." The boys could hear the low growling in the cave getting fainter all the time. "Go throw a rope around his foot, and we'll drag him out o' there with the horse."

"I never did like bears," Billy protested.

"For cryin' out loud, Billy, the durn thing's dead! Besides, just as soon as we get him back out where I can get a good shot I'll pump another one into him to make dang sure."

There was still a little growlin' coming from the den as Billy reluctantly headed in the door with the loop end of his lariat in his hand. It really didn't take him very long to find a foot and get the rope on it, and it took even less time for him to get back out.

"OK, Billy ... pull 'im out!!"

As soon as the rope tightened up around his ankle, the growling got louder and the rope started to jerk violently as Mr. Bruin tried to kick it off.

"He dang shore don't look very dead to me!" Billy squeaked, his face white as a ghost.

"Aw, they do that sometimes just before they croak. Go get your horse and pull him out of there."

This was the only part of this whole operation that Billy thought MIGHT be a good idea. He certainly felt a whole lot more comfortable on horseback than he did afoot.

Billy took his dallies and pointed his horse between a couple of trees. As soon as the slack came out of the rope, the grumbling from the cave got louder again.

"OK! Pull 'im out!" Dick ordered, staring down his gun barrel.

Billy put the spurs to his horse and headed for Texas with a mad bear on the end of his rope. Not only was Mr. Bear not a happy camper, he wasn't even wounded. The boys found themselves with a very healthy and torqued-off bear on the end of their rope. Things got a little hectic there for a minute or two, but Dick finally got off a couple of good shots. Mr. Bear was now dead for sure.

It wasn't until then they discovered that there were actually TWO bears in that hole. One of them WAS dead, but Billy had put his rope around the live one's foot.

"Holy Cow! You could o' got killed in there! Wasn't ya scared?" Dick asked his pardner when the dust had finally settled.

"Naw," Billy lied through his teeth. "I was just in kind of a hurry so I put the rope on the first foot I found ... never did like bears much, though."

106

Chapter Nineteen

Givin' a Little Back

*D*on't you just love the Christmas holidays? By that time of year most of us have pretty well given up on all the work we had planned for the fall season (to be totally honest, we really didn't think we'd ever get it all done anyway), and we take a little time to kick back and relax and be thankful for what we have.

A lot of the rest of the year we're just too durn busy trying to stay on top of the work that's piling up in front of us to even think about it, but come Thanksgiving and Christmas, we can take a little time off to sit by the fire and sort of put everything back into perspective.

Generally, we all have a disappointment or two lurking around in the back of our hat someplace. Maybe we've lost someone, or have gotten a bad report from the doctor, or maybe it just didn't rain on time (again). But, no matter what kind of ruts you've encountered in the trail you've just come down, the secret is in keeping it all in perspective.

That's one of the things I think I've finally gotten a handle on after all these years. If a fella will just start thankin' God for the things we HAVE, all of a sudden every one of those good reasons we've figured out for feeling down in the dumps just sorta disappears. We've all got a lot more than we really need.

We can learn a lot from kids if we'll just take the time. Christmas is really all about kids, isn't it? What ever you do, don't make the mistake of spending too much money on 'em. I don't know how many times I've seen ours pull some expensive gadget out of a box and then throw it in the corner and play in the box. They would have been just as happy with a big empty box wrapped in pretty paper that needed rippin' off.

The real trick for us "long in the tooth folks" is to somehow catch a little glimpse of Christmas from a kid's point of view. That's really all it takes. True fulfillment only comes from capturing the awe and wonderment that comes so naturally to a child and translating it into doing something meaningful for someone else.

Here's a true story. Although I've got a bad reputation (somehow??) of sprinkling a liberal amount of BS in my stories, this one is exactly the way it happened ... honest. I'm just going to change the names for obvious reasons. The only way I even caught wind of this whole deal was by getting to know the guy that was on the receiving end of this little tale after it happened.

Here's how the story unfolded:

Earl was a simple man with a wife and a couple of kids. A few years ago they lived just down the river from us in a farm house they'd rented. He was a good hard worker and provided well for his family, but he'd lost his job, and things were getting pretty tight around that camp.

Earl was quite a hunter, so there really wasn't any danger of them starving to death, but work is awfully hard to find around here in the winter time. There sure wasn't going to be anything extra for Christmas that year.

He was also a proud man. Not the kind of a guy that went around tellin' folks his troubles and asking for a handout. In fact, that was totally out of the question. They'd get by somehow. He gathered scrap iron for a few bucks to pay the light bill, and although everyone was getting sort of sick of venison three times a day, they were scraping by ... barely.

The big problem for Earl was that Christmas was coming. There isn't anything that will take the wind out of a man's sails like not being able to properly provide for his family. Christmas time can be pretty tough in a deal like that.

Bob and Betty somehow got wind of their predicament. They weren't folks of enormous means, by any stretch of the imagination, but they had made a practice of trying to find a family like Earl's to bless every Christmas.

Bob operated a small business, and Betty was a stay-at-home Mom and a great cook. It was just a little special something that they had been doing for quite some time, but managed to keep it entirely to themselves. It was their annual secret mission. They did it on the sly ... very few folks, except the ones that they'd helped over the years, even knew what was going on.

They'd somehow managed to find out how many kids Earl and his wife had, and their sizes, and just "showed up" one night after supper with a whole car load of goodies. I think there were new school coats for the kids, and I know there was a little toy or two.

They also had in tow several boxes that contained a huge turkey with all the trimmin's, a sack of spuds and a thousand other little treats; and those little things were the most special of all. They're the kinds of things a family with a real job would just normally take for granted. Whatever money Bob and Betty spent must have seemed like peanuts compared to the looks in the eyes of Earl's family that cold snowy night so many years ago.

That's the true spirit of Christmas ... helping to light a spark of hope and childish awe in the eyes of someone who needs a little boost of encouragement. In some cases, they may be just about ready to give up entirely.

This year when Christmas rolls around again, go do something nice for someone who doesn't expect it ... and if you want a REAL blessing ... keep it a secret.

Chapter Twenty

Flyin' High

"*D*oggone it, Dick but this necktie and these new boots are killin' me," Billy complained as the boys rattled down the highway.

"Maybe so, but you look purty sharp for an ol' cowpuncher," Dick reassured his pardner. *Hiccup.* "... 'sides an impotent feller like you that's goin' all the way to California needs to look impotent."

"You sure you can handle the calvin' all by yerself? I shore hate to leave you all alone this time of year. If 'n it wasn't that it was little Katy's weddin', I wouldn't go a'tall. She's my favert niece, ya know, an' I just can't hardly miss it. I shore hope she ain't marryin' one o' them freaks with ear rings an' a tooty-fruity hair do. What time do I need to get on that durn airplane anyway?"

"Not 'til almost dinner time, and we only got a couple o' hours to go. We'll make 'er all right. *Hiccup.* Pass me over a little more breakfast."

Billy screwed the lid off another long-necked breakfast beverage and passed it across the seat. "Aahh ... the Breakfast of Champions," Dick gulped.

The sun was just streakin' the eastern sky on its way over here from Africa or wherever it goes at night, and it was at least a hundred more miles to the airport. The time passed quickly enough. It was usually only two six packs or so from home to the airport, and they were there before you know it.

Billy did look pretty good in his new store bought suit and his new boots, even if they did make him feel a little uncomfortable. The boys gathered his suitcase out of the back of the old pickup and headed into the Billings airline terminal.

"Don't forget to give me yer pocket knife. You 'member what happened that other time. I thought they was gonna lock you up."

"DANG IT," Billy belched as he handed his trusty Old Timer to his pal. "I feel like I fergot my pants without my pocketknife. I still wonder just how many cowboys has ever tried to high-jack a airplane. This is just plain dumb. Don't you dare lose that thing. It was my Grandad's ... and I had it for 40 years."

"I wont lose 'er. 'Sides, rules is rules. You wanna ride their airplane you gotta do like they say. She's a purty long walk to California ... don't want to miss the weddin'."

"Yea, yea."

The security check went without a hitch ... well almost. When Billy had to take off his boots and his hat and his belt buckle to get through the metal detector. He almost came uncorked, but then he remembered the last time he'd offered to rearrange the inspector's face and how he almost wound up in the pokey over it. He just gritted his teeth and bore the indignity.

Probably the only thing to save him was the fact that this inspector was a cute little dark eyed gal with a nice smile. Billy even tried a little joke or two on her, but really didn't get very far.

He waved goodbye to his ol' pard and sat down to wait for the time to board the plane. It wasn't long until one of the airline staff informed him that his seat had been upgraded to First Class because they wanted to accommodate their customers, and as the lady said, "We suggest suits and ties for our First Class passengers, and because your professional image is just what our airline is seeking, you have been chosen for an upgrade."

"Dick was right," Billy thought to himself, "I DO look impotent." (He almost brought up the pocketknife deal to the attendant, but wisely decided at the last minute not to.)

It wasn't long until it was time to board the plane, and much to Billy's inflated ego, the First Class passengers were at the head of the line. He straightened himself to the tallest proportions possible, sucked in his belly and made his way to his seat at the front of the plane. He was a little disappointed that his seat partner wasn't one of those good lookin', long-legged blonde movie starlet types like he'd hoped, but he settled down in the roomy First Class cabin to await take off.

The guy in the seat next to him was a sort of sophisticated lookin' fella in a high priced suit and kind of a sour-puss look on his face. Didn't look like he'd done a day's work in his life to Billy, but he thought he might just get a few tips from him on actin' impotent. After all, he WAS goin' to California.

Shortly after takeoff, the plane got to cruisin' altitude and a pretty stewardess came by to ask if they wanted a complimentary drink from the bar.

"Are you kiddin'?" Billy thought to himself. "Is the Pope a Catholic? Man, this high-society stuff is even better than I had it figgered." He finally regained his composure from the combination of the pretty lady's liquid eyes and his elation over a free drink, and ordered the most sophisticated soundin' thing on the menu. (Although he didn't have a clue what it was ... some cowboys 'll drink almost anything.)

"And you, sir," the stewardess inquired of the pickle-faced guy in the next seat.

"Miss, I would prefer to be accosted by a dozen brazen harlots than to ever have alcohol cross my lips."

Billy just starred at him two-eyed for a second, trying to figure out exactly what all of those fifty-cent words meant. Finally, he spoke up. "Me too, Ma'am. I guess I'll jus' change my order ... didn't know we had a choice."

"You really oughta clean up more often, Billy.
You don't look all that bad in a necktie."

114

Chapter Twenty One

Buyin' the Right Parts

I'm not sure this outfit would survive without my little wifey. I sure hope she doesn't read this. She's liable to hit me up for a raise or something. But then on the other hand, if I doubled her wages it still wouldn't amount to all that much. Two times nuthin' is still nuthin'.

She's sure been an asset around here. If something needs doin' I know I can always count on her to give it her best shot. She's not just a little piece of fluff, but because she IS little and cute, I've gotten her to successfully take things back to the store when I know they would have turned me down.

"Ma, why don't you fix your hair and get yourself all triggered up and take that gizmo back to the store for me?"

"I thought you special ordered that thing. You know they won't take it back."

"They probably wouldn't take it back from ME, but if you just bat your eyes at 'em a time or two, it'll probably work." ... and it did on more than one occasion.

We had sort of a wreck happen out here a few years ago. We bought a hay baler from a dealer that told us that "it had just been through the shop" ... yea, right. There was still a rock in the bale chamber when we got it home. A week or so later, we had tons of hay to bale and the durn thing broke down ... again, so while I tore it apart, I sent my little sweetie after the parts we needed with the strict orders not to come home without them.

"What if they don't have them?"

"Then just have 'em tear it off of one of the balers out in their lot. We need that stuff NOW."

On that particular occasion, her sweet little demure smile and batting eyes just weren't quite adequate to get the job done. Never fear. A ranch wife has to be resourceful. Although the baler store didn't have the needed parts in stock, and the parts man initially refused to rob one of the balers on the lot, Sweetie drove back in the yard with just what I needed. Because this is a G rated column, I can't tell you exactly where she told the fuming parts manager she was going to drive that "just through the shop" baler of his, (You'll have to use your imagination) but wherever it was must not have sounded all that comfortable, because she got the parts she went after. She might be little, but I'm even smart enough not to cross her.

Bless her heart, but she tends to get words a little mixed up sometimes, and there are times when the things she says don't quite come out right, and the result is completely hilarious. As a matter of fact, I've called her my own personal "Home Entertainment Center" on many occasions, and she never lets me down. Not long ago we had a neighbor in the kitchen that was having a few health problems, and she was admonishing him to make sure that he thoroughly questioned the doctor on his next visit.

"You ask a lot of questions. After all it's your health that's at stake, and you know what they say, "The squeaky wheel gets the ... the ... the ... the WORM."

I must have laughed for ten minutes over that one. The really funny part was that she didn't even know what she'd said for a day or two, and would have sworn that that's the way that old saying goes.

That little habit of hers really got me in a mess once. We needed to go to Great Falls for something about ten days in the future, and I made the mistake of telling her that the alternator belt on the car wasn't all that good and maybe I should change it before we made the trip. The vision of a busted fan belt out on the road with a couple of little kids in the car is not a pretty sight.

Nearly a week had passed since I first mentioned the faulty belt to her, and she kept reminding me that I'd said it needed changing. "Don't forget you said you were going to change that altimeter belt before we leave." (For the mechanically challenged among us, an altimeter is the little dial in an airplane that tells you how high you're flying. They don't even HAVE a belt.)

I got a real chuckle out of that one, but not wanting to hurt her feelings, I didn't correct her. For three or four days before we left on our little excursion, I was reminded several times a day about our worn out "altimeter belt", and each time I kept my chuckles to myself.

I never did get around to changing the durn thing, so on the way through town as she was reminding me for the 'leventeenth time, I thought I'd just pick one up at a parts place so we'd have a spare in case of a breakdown.

This was back at the tail end of the "Flower Power" days of the early seventies, and the store I chose had a real Zero behind the parts counter. I think he was a poster child for the drug burn-out program.

Just the looks of the guy had my red-neck hackles up, and the cook's naggin' about the parts we needed probably didn't help my attitude any. But then, how difficult can finding me a fan belt be? Even this guy should be able to handle that, I thought.

They say if you tell a lie enough times that you'll even believe it yourself after a while, and apparently that's the case. I walked right up to the counter and asked the used up old hippie for an altimeter belt.

"A what?"

"An altimeter belt for a 69 Chevy." (Boy, this guy is even a bigger idiot that he looks, I thought to myself. He doesn't even know what an altimeter belt is.)

"You got an altimeter in that thing? Whoooaaa duuude!"

Of course in retrospect, this guy was used to flying pretty high, so he probably thought something like that just might come in handy in that chartreuse micro-bus he floated around town in. He starts excitedly paging through his parts book to find the right parts.

"You musta put that on yourself ... there's not anything about that in the book."

"How in the dickens does this joker keep this job," I thought to myself. "If he can't even find something simple like this, how in the world does he find something a little more technical?"

"Of course I bought it that way! They've ALL got one!" I spewed. Back to the book he went.

He finally gave up looking, and I turned on my heel and left in frustration. "There's no use even trying to do business with an idiot, I'm never coming back in this place," I said to myself.

As the door closed behind me, and I repeated "Altimeter Belt!" to myself one more time, I at long last figured out who the idiot was. I'd heard it so many times that I'd just repeated what I'd heard.

I'm a man of my convictions, though. I swore I'd never go back in that place for parts again, and I never did.

I was afraid someone might recognize me.

119

"I just HATE that!

Us girls get blamed for everything."

Chapter Twenty Two

The Nitro Solution

*U*nlike a few folks I know, I'm not the kind of a fella that is continually wantin' the government to do something for me. I'd rather they just did the really big things like keepin' Osama and the rest of the Bin Laden boys out of my hay corrals. The little stuff we seem to handle just fine. As a matter of fact, most of the time I wish they'd just go away and leave me alone.

In my humble opinion, America sure has slid a long ways downhill. In the old days there was a stigma attached to taking a handout, and for an able bodied man to take one was criminal. Things have sure changed, and it's certainly not all for the better. The poor guys that hold public office must get awfully sick of the long line out in front of their office door with their hands out.

So what in the world does a radical thinkin' guy like me do if he has a problem (that government created)

121

that he needs the government to fix? I really hate complainers. I'm pretty hesitant to do much of that, but I just found a solution to our little dilemma, and it might even work for you if you can figure out a way to adapt it to your situation.

A few years ago some shave-tail inspector from the Montana State Department of Insanity told the county boys that they would have to tear out the perfectly good bridge on the county road that runs by our place and replace it. In all fairness, from their perspective, they probably thought it needed replacing. But then from mine, nobody had ever fallen through it, and the inspector guys that make those decisions don't have to pay the bills.... we do. That leaves the official county boys with no choice but to follow big brother's directive: "CHANGE IT NOW." So change it they did, and the result was a real wreck.

The idea was OK ... it just didn't work. In order to save us taxpayers a little money, the boys got a couple of railroad flat cars and put them in side by side. Apparently it's strong enough ... nobody ever fell through it. Of course, nobody ever fell through the old one either. The problem was the top. It was slick half inch steel plate that banged and clattered when you walked across it. That works just fine for a vehicle, but just TRY chasin' a cow across it. It'd been that way for a couple of years.

I told you that I hate complainers, and the Good Lord knows there are probably enough of those in line at the court house now, so I'd just casually mention our little "problem" to Art when I'd run into him.

Art Kleinjan is my official county commissioner. I've known him for a long time. In fact, I knew him back in the old days when he still did an honest day's work. He reminds me a lot of Will Rogers.

He and ol' Will have a lot in common. They're both cowboys, and Will said once: "I ain't the member of any organized political party ... I'm a Democrat." So is Art. Through the years I've tried real hard not to hold that against him.

Art Kleinjan

"Yea, we need to do somethin' about that bridge. We'll get to it. Just don't give up," was the answer Art always came back with, but nothing ever happened, and time just kept draggin' on.

That's when I came up with my ingenious plan to push him over dead center and get the bridge fixed. I've got this locoed horse that I got in an even swap for a ridin' lawn mower. If it hadn't been for health reasons, I never would have traded. I sure got the short end, that's for sure.

I did it for the little woman. I noticed she was puttin' on a little weight, and so I figured if I traded off her ridin' mower, the old push one would trim her right back up. It worked too, but old Nitro (the horse I got in the trade) leaves a lot to be desired.

I called Art on the phone and asked him to come out. Of course, politicians are always looking forward to another election, so he agreed right away. It was a nice sunny morning as he rattled and clattered across the disaster they called a bridge out in front of the house.

I had ol' Nitro all saddled up when he drove in the yard.

"You say you need a little help?" Art asked with a big dumb Democratic grin on his face.

"Yea, I can't seem to get that bull across the bridge," I answered pointing to a critter in the pasture across the creek. "I was wonderin' if maybe I could get a hand. Here, you can just take Ol' Nitro and ride across the bridge and get him for me."

Nitro is really pretty scary looking. There are lots of times that ridin' lawn mower would look pretty good again. He was standing there sweatin' and shiverin' at the same time with only the whites of his eyes showing and about six inches of slack between the back of the saddle and his boney old back. As I handed Art the reins, Ol' Nitro pulled back and threw himself over backwards and started beatin' his head on the ground.

124

"He'll be alright in a minute," I assured my cowboy friend turned politician, "sometimes he just does that for some reason."

Art isn't a quitter, and if anybody could have ridden Nitro across that bridge it probably would have been him. BUT ... he's also smart enough to get elected three or four times, so he ain't no dummy. His eyes got just about the same size as Nitro's. He took one look at that locoed horse beatin' his head on the ground and another at that slick topped rattle-bang bridge and suddenly thought of pressing government business that needed his immediate attention.

"Doggone it, Kenny, I just haven't got the time this mornin'," Art apologized as he climbed back in his pickup and Nitro staggered back to his feet, quiverin' and looking at the ground. "There's a big meeting I really need to be at about five minutes ago."

There was a familiar clatter-bang from the bridge and a cloud of dust as my old friend turned politician sped back to the relatively safe confines of county bureaucracy. My plan worked like a charm. The bridge was fixed the next day.

Nitro has served his purpose, and Ma's about got herself back in racin' shape. Has anybody got a bridge that needs fixin'? I'll trade a heck of a good horse for a ridin' lawn mower.

"So THAT'S where you got ol' Nitro.
I wuz wonderin' what ever happened
to our lawnmower."

Chapter
Twenty Three

Lucky Billy

I'm not a real big movie go-er, but one of the ones I remember from the foggy expanse that occasionally serves as my memory was one called *The Sting*. You don't have to worry about me giving you the whole rundown ... I couldn't remember enough of it to do it justice anyway. Besides, nobody hates second hand movies more than I do, so I'll spare you the pain.

I DO remember the main thrust of the plot, though. It was about a bad guy that was set up and summarily fleeced by a bunch of cons in an elaborate scheme. I guess maybe I liked it so well because it appeals to a part of my criminal nature that perhaps more than just a few of you share. Ever'one likes to see a bad guy get what he's got comin', even if you have to bend the law a little to give it to him.

Here's a couple of sayin's for you: "All's fair in love and war," and "It really ain't a sin to steal from a thief." I know you've heard the first one, and the second one is a little snatch of one-eyed wisdom that I'll share from under my hat. That's the premise of the movie, and what this little story is all about.

Now Billy really isn't a bad guy. At least not like the guy in the movie, but he was doing a bunch of braggin' about how lucky he was, so his ol' buddy Dick set him up and beat him out of a couple hundred bucks ... just to give him a little dose of badly over-due humility. After all, what are friends for?

The two old bachelor cowboys were on their way down to Nevada in their old rattle trap pickup a few years ago and Billy was continually crowin' about how lucky he was and that Dick just might learn a thing or two if he'd pay close attention when they reached all of those casinos.

"Dad blame it, Billy," Dick answered his braggin' partner, "you ain't so lucky. If you was lucky, you'd be rich by now."

"When it comes to cards and games and stuff like that I'm the luckiest guy alive," Billy snorted back.

"You don't know sick-'im from come-here," Dick snapped. "I'll tell you what I'll do. I'll betcha a hunerd bucks you lose the first deal you get into when we roll into town."

"That 'll be like takin' candy from a baby! I'll jus' take that dumb bet o' yers.... an' what's more I'll betcha a hunerd more you jus' made a bad bet!"

"Yer on!"

Little did Billy know he'd just been slickered; humility lesson number one, coming right up. He'd never even set foot in Elko, Nevada before and because Dick knew the place pretty well, he immediately set his plan into motion. He wheeled the old pickup into a grocery store and came back out with a twelve pack of Billy's favorite liquid refreshment.

"I thought you might be gettin' a little dry," Dick grinned to himself as Billy eagerly ripped the cardboard off his new prize. "We'll be to town in about an hour and a half." Billy took the bait hook line and sinker ... just like his pardner knew he would. There's a few things a fella can always count on and Billy's unquenchable thirst is one of them.

As the lights of the outskirts of Elko peeked over the horizon, Dick's plan was right on schedule. Billy was needin' to find a restroom pretty bad. He'd asked Dick to pull over a couple of times already, but always got the excuse that they were almost there, so maybe he should wait.

"Don't forget our bet, now," Dick reminded his pardner as they went into the little place he'd specifically chosen.

"I ain't forgot! I'll be right back and take yer money. Right now I've got more important things on my mind!" Billy headed to the rear of the establishment towards the neon sign that indicated where the restrooms were.

"I'll wait right here," Dick called over Billy's shoulder. "You can pay up as soon as you lose that first game."

It was the perfect setup. Little did Billy know that Dick had picked the specific place to stop, exactly where Billy would need to go when they got there, and precisely what he'd do that would make Dick his two hundred bucks.

Billy simply didn't have all the facts to make an intelligent decision. The urinals in the establishment Dick had chosen were each equipped with a little

129

fake fly about halfway up on the inside. That little fly was so wired that when it came into contact with Billy's recycled liquid refreshment, it completed an electrical circuit that turned on all of the neon lights in the entire place, and activated the sign above the bar that read: "You lose! Score: Fly 876542, Cowboys 0."

Billy made his way back to where he'd left his old pardner to the sounds of bells, whistles and applause, with Dick proudly pointing at the flashing "You Lose!" sign behind the bar.

"Well, well if it ain't Lucky Billy! Looks like you owe me two hunerd bucks!"

For some reason, humility is always a lot more fun when it happens to someone else.

"Well, they DO call me Lucky Billy.
If you're so smart an' I'm so dumb ...
How come YOU'RE choppin' the wood?"

Chapter
Twenty Four

Don't Cross Irene

Probably most of us have been accused of talkin' when we should have been listenin' a few times, but I think Spud Malone just learned a lesson that he'll not soon forget. At least, he sure seems to watch the way he talks around his little honey a lot closer than he used to.

Spud has always been a little reckless with his mouth. In fact there were times it was downright embarrassing the way that he'd talk to his wife, Irene. Most of the neighbor women couldn't even stand to be around him because of it, and the men didn't think too highly of him for it either. That's probably why the whole neighborhood sent up a cheer when they heard that little Irene "gave ol' Spud his."

Some of Irene's closest friends even encouraged her to pack her stuff and look for greener pastures, but her answer was always the same. "Ah, that's just Spud. He really don't mean nothin' by it."

Time didn't seem to help the situation much, either. I've seen some of those salty old cusses sort of mellow out as they got a little older, but it sure hasn't been the case in that camp. If anything, his demeaning attitude even seemed to get a little worse. The straw that broke the camel's back was a remark or two he made to her a couple of weeks ago at a big pot luck get together in town.

I think that gravity, time, and Mother Nature have this conspiracy going to screw up our once sleek racehorse physiques, and of course, Irene isn't any exception. Even if a person stays in pretty good shape like she has, everything tends to get sort of re-arranged into a little less desirable package as we get older.

Us men now, we tend to turn out just like old bulls; a bad attitude and a big belly. And the ladies ... well, I'm even smart enough not to tie into that subject, but everything sort of heads south for them too, and they tend to be a little more sensitive about those inevitable changes.

Spud and Irene had taken one of their little granddaughters to the potluck, and just before the food line formed, Spud made mistake number one. Little Katy was diggin' through Grandma's purse for a piece of gum when she came out with a little blue lidded bottle. "What's this for Gammy?" the little innocent questioned.

"Oh, that's just the stuff Gammy uses to get rid of her wrinkles," Irene answered.

(Boys, let me tell you just in case you're not bright enough to have figured it out yet ... wrinkles and a lady's name are two words you NEVER use in the same sentence.)

"Shore don't look like it's workin' does it, Katy? Har! Har! Har!" Spud exploded in his usual brash insensitivity.

Irene just bit her lip. She probably would have cried if she'd not been in public, but as usual, she didn't even answer the thoughtless jerk.

Spud's second and perhaps final mistake, came towards the end of the potluck line. As Irene was dishing up a scrumptious looking piece of cheese cake, ol' Spud just couldn't control his flappin' jaws again. Gazing down at her jeans that were a couple of sizes bigger than the ones she'd worn a few months earlier he cracked, "Why bother eatin' that stuff? You oughta just rub it on yer hips and save it the trip ... that's where it's gonna wind up anyway."

Oh, boy ... little did he know that he'd just driven Spud Malone's final coffin nail.

They say that revenge is sweet, and Irene must have been thinking about this one for a while. Her plan was ever' bit as sweet as that cheese cake. She had an old friend that owned a well bred but "rotten to the core" spoiled buckin' horse that was a dead ringer for Tony, the Hancock bred Quarter Horse that Spud rode. About ten days ago she arranged for him to be delivered in the middle of the night and tied in Tony's stall. The friend then turned Tony back out into the horse pasture.

This spoiled bronc was not only a perfect match for Spud's horse, but he'd stand just like an angel while you saddled him, and let a fella get right on without a problem. The rub came when you asked him to move. Oh, he'd move all right ... about fifteen feet straight up, swap ends in mid-air, and then stampede for Texas buckin' and bawlin'.

Bright and early the next morning, Big Mouth Spud had a field full of cows to move and a few of the neighbors over to help. There aren't any lights in the barn, which helped the ruse along just fine. I'm not sure if any of the other boys were in on the prank or not, but Irene was standing right there in the moonlight to take it all in. She certainly wasn't disappointed.

Tony's replacement was a perfect gentleman, taking the saddle in the strange barn without even a hint that he wasn't the real thing. Spud casually stepped on board, flappin' his jaws to the neighbors as usual. The rest is history.

A blow by blow description of the ensuing ride is a little difficult, given the dim morning light, but there was a yard full of witnesses to what happened. Spud was launched fifteen or twenty feet straight into the air, landing flat on his back in the dirt in front of the barn. As he slowly sat up, rubbin' his head and muttering to himself, Irene was right there in the front row of chucklin' cowboys with a little overdue verbal turpentine for his wounded pride. She'd been savin' up for this for a long time.

"Instead of even tryin' to get on your horse, you oughta just sit on yer butt in the dirt. That's where you're gonna wind up anyway ... might as well save yourself the trip!"

Revenge IS sweet.

Chapter
Twenty Five

Smooth Takeoffs ~ Bumpy Landings

I was just doing a little thinkin' about my Dad. I'm better off than a few folks I know in a couple of respects. First, mine is still alive (a great feat in itself for an 80 some year old crop duster), and I don't even have to think too hard to find something nice to say about him. I know everyone isn't that fortunate.

On the other hand, I'm not sure if my Dad is extra-brave or just crazy. They say it isn't an absolute prerequisite for an aerial spray pilot to be nuts, but it sure helps. Basic laws of heredity and genetics also prove that kids tend to take after their Dads, and that "Nuts don't fall far from the tree" ... that may literally help to explain some of my strange behavior. If I act a little nuts now and then, well maybe I come by it honestly.

A twist of fate made Dad miss his real calling. He wanted in the worst way to fly a fighter plane in World War II. Unfortunately for him, Uncle Sam felt that he would be a greater asset to the war effort to stay home and help my Grandad raise meat and potatoes. Soldiers need to eat as well as shoot.

We all have dreams that don't come true I guess, and not having the opportunity to show the Army Air Corps what he was made of has always been a big disappointment for Dad. He gets a little miffed at times when he hears about an old military veteran getting cut rates on prescriptions while he pays full price.

"I think I did ever' bit as much to help the war effort as Ol' What's-His-Name."

I agree. Life isn't always fair.

Dad took up aerial spraying as the next best option, and he must have been a good one. There's no such thing as a bad, old spray pilot. He finally sold his airplane last summer, and almost cried when it took off from his short little country airstrip carved out of a hay field. Mom was tickled pink. I think she figured that all of those years listening and praying for that familiar engine drone to bring her man safely home again were enough.

All of her fears weren't just female overkill either. He had several close calls and tore up more that one plane. Undoubtedly the worst wreck happened west of Chester a few years ago when Dad was spraying wheat for my uncle. Shortly after loading up and taking off from a little road in between the strips of farming, things started to go haywire.

He'd only gained about a hundred feet of altitude when a little pin fell out of the cable that controlled the ailerons on the wings. The plane started into a slow turn to the right, and Dad was helpless to do anything about it.

He could still make the plane go up and down, and as it was just a matter of time until he hit the ground anyway, he made the split second decision to head it back towards the earth and attempt a landing in the wheat field. It's just that kind of thinkin' in a tight place that would have made Dad a whale of an asset to the Army Air Corps.

Unfortunately the out of control airplane was banking more steeply to the right all the time, and the landing really wasn't one of his smoothest. The first thing to hit the ground was the right wing tip, followed immediately by the nose and the engine.

Dow Overcast on the Home Place
With His Cessna Ag Truck

137

Next to make contact with Mother Earth was the left wing tip with the tail section waiting in line for its turn. If not a perfect landing, at least it was a perfect cartwheel.

Parts of what used to be an airplane were scattered over a hundred yards of northern Montana with biggest remaining piece being the cage containing the seat and that day's luckiest spray pilot. All he got was a little knot on his head.

Mom is always quick to tell everyone that luck didn't have anything to do with it. "I've been praying for that crazy man for sixty years. That's ALL that saved him."

Just because Dad sold his spray plane doesn't mean that Mom can slack off on those prayers just yet. He took part of the money and bought a motorcycle. I'm not too sure the plane ever put him in the hospital, but that durn motorcycle sure did. He got it all tangled up with a tree. It was a lot like the airplane deal. The takeoff went OK but the landing was less than perfect.

I was in his hospital room and took the call when the phone rang. It was the lady from admissions wanting to verify some of his information.

"He fell and broke a leg ... is that right?"

"Well, not exactly. He was riding a motorcycle and fell out of a tree."

"You're kidding, right? A motorcycle??? How old did you say he was?"

"He'll be 81 in August."

You boys at The Army Air Corps really dropped the ball. If you're still looking for a few good men, he'll only be 83 on his next birthday. He's all healed up, now ... good as new again ... and he'd still like to take a crack at a P51.

Chapter Twenty Six

Paintin' The Biffy

*T*here's not anyone that likes being embarrassed. As I stop and think a minute on a couple of the more uncomfortable things I've been through, my face gets red just thinkin' about them.

But then on the other hand, a person with a depraved criminal mind such as I have been blessed with, can somehow find glee and immense satisfaction in trapping some poor innocent soul in an embarrassing situation ... IF (and only if) it can be justified in my own twisted thought patterns that they somehow have it coming.

Miss Blackstone was just such a person, bless her cold old heart. Every time I think of embarrassment, and someone who must have deserved it, she's one of the first ones that comes to mind. I didn't personally have anything to do with setting up her confrontation with humiliation, but it's only because I didn't think of it. A couple of other guys beat me to it.

Miss Blackstone was an old maid school teacher with the disposition of a cornered badger and a vile hatred for disruptive male children. In most schools I'm aware of, that constitutes approximately half of the entire student body. Her extreme detestation for the boys didn't seem to translate into favorable treatment for the girls, either. She was just plain mean. I guess I'd have to say she was just about the perfect target.

Why in the dickens she would volunteer to help out at a church youth camp defies all logic. Although it was obvious to everyone she absolutely hated kids ... there she was. To give her the benefit of the doubt (in retrospect) she probably thought she might actually have a hand in reforming some of the little monsters.

Unfortunately, even church camps seem to have their fair share of adolescent hoodlums. Usually Mom and Dad think, and probably rightfully so, that it would be a great environment and a good influence on their precious little Johnny, who at the moment seems destined to be in prison by the time he's old enough to shave.

It was two just such inmates ... oops, I mean campers ... that devised the perfect plan to dethrone and totally humiliate the ornery and sanctimonious Miss Blackstone. Boy, I wish I could have been in on this one.

This happened several years ago at a rather primitive camp back in the woods. The two boys "borrowed" the sound amplifier and a microphone from the hall where the evening meetings took place, and fastened the speaker down under the old wooden seat in the outdoor biffy. They cleverly concealed the wire from the speaker in the grass and waited in some nearby bushes for their victim to approach.

She bolted out the biffy door, screaming hysterically.

When nature calls even kings and Miss Blackstone must answer eventually, and it wasn't long until the prim and proper lady with the snarl on her lips and a heart chiseled out of pure ice came down the faithful little path to the outdoor facility. After waiting just the proper amount of time for the lady to be about her personal business, the boys sprang into action. One of them flipped the little switch and with the deepest voice he could muster, growled into the microphone.

"Hey, lady! Do you mind movin'? We're tryin' to paint down here, and you're shuttin' off all the light!"

Miss Blackstone was immediately dethroned in more ways than one. She burst out of that biffy door on a dead run, with her disheveled wardrobe only partially intact. The normally pickle faced old prude was suddenly distraught, screaming hysterically, and was quite surprised to be greeted with the cheers and applause of a large audience of degenerate adolescent church campers gathered specifically to witness her disgraceful demise.

It couldn't have happened to a nicer lady. I wish I'd o' thought of that.

"Now that's disgusting."

Chapter
Twenty Seven

Bar Stool Calvin'

I always look forward to Spring. All the new life with the calves being born and the grass trying to turn green just gives a fella hope that things just might work out one more year. Even though I look forward to it, at least in the beginning, by the time the first of May rolls around, I'd sell that calvin' job pretty cheap.

From around the 15th of April on is how you tell the cowboys from the farmers. There are lots of cowboys with farmin' to do, and a lot of farmers that have cows, but that time of year is what really separates them.

A real farmer's cows are on their own just as soon as the fields are dry enough not to bog a tractor down, and cowboys always get their crop in AFTER the cows are all taken care of. Sometimes that's not until the first of June or so.

Now, I can't figure how a bachelor manages calving at all. If I didn't have the cook to help out around here, I'm not too sure we'd have ever made it. This was the very subject of a rather heated, although good natured discussion a few years ago.

Paul and Dennis are both single. They've each got their own outfit so they both have to shoulder the entire responsibility for every one of their "heifer checks." Because it's easier to just stay up than it is to go to bed and then try to get back up, the boys would do a check around eight o'clock or so and then putt into town and meet at a local pub.

The neighborhood waterin' holes actually do a pretty good business during calving season, as this is pretty customary in more than one community out this way. These local establishments aren't exactly those "necktie only" joints, either. The calving clientele tends to be more the five buckle overshoe crowd, easily distinguishable by their distinct aroma of digested hay and retained placenta.

"How's she goin'?" Paul queries from his barstool as Dennis trudges slowly in the door.

Both of the guys had been calvin' for a month or so, and they were beginning to show the wear of too much work and not enough sleep.

"Not so good ... I just lost one. I was right there too, but the little bugger was backwards and I just couldn't save 'im."

"Doggone it, I lost one this mornin' the same way ... guess you can't save 'em all."

Just then Les comes in the door. His cows had only been calvin' a week or so, and he was still feeling pretty frisky.

144

"What 're you boys doin' in town? I thought you was calvin'." After some good natured joshing Les announced that he was calvin' too, but that his little honey was lookin' after things. The neighbors had a big time visiting and tellin' yarns, and not surprisingly, they almost had the entire bar to themselves. Their fragrance was just a little more than most of the town folks could handle.

Along about eleven or so Paul and Dennis are both eyeing the clock and gettin' a little on the nervous side. "Gotta go," one of the boys announced. "Can't afford to lose a calf sittin' on this dang barstool."

"Me too," chimed in his partner as he stood and headed for the door. "You comin', Les?"

"Heck no ... the ol' lady has the 'leven o'clock check. I'll just stay here an' take care of things for you boys. Ours don't need checkin' again until they throw me out o' here at two. You guys have to find yourself a couple o' cooks ... that's what you need!" Les joshed as the two tired bachelors trudged out the door and back into the brisk evening air. "Have fun!" he taunted, raising his glass in salute. "If you was as good lookin' as me you'd o' had a woman by now."

As Paul neared his pickup, he stopped right in his tracks and began to giggle to himself.

"What's so funny?" Dennis questioned.

"That dang Les thinks he's so smart," he laughed. "Good lookin', my foot! That knuckle-head ... he thinks he can ranch from that durn barstool while we're out here bustin' our rear ends. I jus' got a plan to fix his wagon."

Here's what happened. The boys each went home to their bone pile and threw a couple of dead calves in the back of their pickup, and headed over to Les' calvin' pasture. They knew that his little darlin' would have checked the cows at eleven, so by midnight the coast would be clear. (They also KNEW where Les would be for a couple more hours.) They drove into the pasture and distributed the little lifeless carcasses around at random, being oh so careful not to leave any tell-tale tracks in the snow.

They put one in the little brush patch, a couple on the big straw mound that Les had conscientiously piled in the middle of the corral, and the last one right by the gate where they were certain their soon to be ex-friend would be sure to find it.

"That'll teach him to crow about his ol' lady doin' all the work. NOW ... I bet we get more sleep tonight than HE does."

Yessiree, that's just what happened, too. Les tromped around in the snow until the sun was coming up, desperately trying to find the Mamas that belonged to the dead babies. He finally smelled a rat about daylight.

He could never seem to find any lonesome Mama cows, and finally noticed that none of the little departed souls had any melted snow around them, and none of 'em were froze down. It only took a couple of days to unravel the mystery and for the boys to 'fess up. They really tried to keep a lid on it, but then ... it was such a good story they just HAD to tell somebody.

Nope, barstool calvin' doesn't ALWAYS work ... no matter how good a woman you've got. Especially if you've got "friends" like Les has.

146

Chapter Twenty Eight

Super Charged Fishin'

"Fishin'? With a hunk o' pipe?" Billy slurred in disbelief as he opened another bottle of Milwaukee's finest to top off his normal liquid breakfast.

"Well, it ain't exac'ly pipe ... That'd be too heavy. Twenty foot of that light little conduit stuff that you run 'lectric wires through is what works the best," his pardner Dick patiently explained. The boys had just about gotten their work caught up on their alkali hard-scrabble outfit, and Dick was suggesting a little adventure.

"How in the heck do you even tie any fishin' string on to a hunk o' pipe? Why don't we jus' cut a willow like we always do?"

"'Cause these are fresh water salmon, and they oughta be runnin' right now. You don't even use a fishin' line. All you gotta do is weld one of them big ol' three pronged hooks on the end o' a long ol' hunk o' conduit an' drag 'em out."

147

"Oh, sure ya can," Billy burped. "I can't even snag a fish in a bucket much less swimmin' up a creek."

"There ain't nuthin' to it. I've done it lots of times. I gar-un-tee you'll get a real charge out of it. We can pull 'em out o' there by the washtub full."

"You sure that's legal?"

"If it ain't, it oughta be ... 'sides since when did legal have anything to do with havin' a little fun?" Dick grinned.

Within an hour the boys were rattlin' their old pickup to Dick's special fishin' spot. It was a few hundred miles from the alkali flats to salmon fishin' so they were loaded down with all of the essentials ... a fryin' pan, washtub for the fish, a loaf o' bread and nine cases of Milwaukee's finest, what else?

"I'm purty dang shure this ain't legal," Billy belched as they pulled in beside a clear little rippling stream. "Shore wish we had a crik like that back home. I get doggone sick o' that alkali coffee."

The boys unloaded and got right to work. Dick had welded his fishin' gear together before they'd left the ranch, and was anxious to show his pardner how it worked.

"OK. You jus' get on yer knees here by the washtub, and when I drag 'em out you pull 'em off the hook an' throw 'em in the tub." He instructed as he snuck up to the edge of the little stream with his home-made fish snagger.

Sure enough ... it worked like a charm. There were fish everywhere. Dick was snaggin' and Billy was so busy fillin' the washtub that he let his liquid lunch get warm in the sun. It wasn't long until they had their washtub about half full and their snaggin' hole about fished out. Right across the creek and upstream just a little bit was another promising looking hole.

148

"Let me do 'er this time," Billy grinned as he chugged down the last of his warm noon meal. He was now totally sold on this new fishin' plan of Dick's, and any faint concerns about the legal technicalities were overshadowed by all the fun they were having. "I'll jus' pull off my boots an' wade over to the other side. That hole over there looks ever' bit as good as this one."

The boys must have been out in the middle of somebody's cow pasture, because there was one saggy string of barbed wire lazily hangin' across the stream that needed crossing. With all the agility of a tight rope walker, Billy used the long metal conduit as a balancing beam and cautiously started into the cool water. The going was pretty slow. The water was only a little over knee deep, but the slick rocks on the stream bed made for poor footing.

Just as Billy went to cross the wire, disaster struck. One foot slid on the slick rocky bottom and the barbed wire made a nearly debilitating connection with the crotch of Billy's jeans and its sensitive contents. It really wasn't the physical connection that was the problem. It was the ELECTRICAL connection. Yep, it was an electric fence. In the excitement of catching all those fish the boys had failed to notice that one itty-bitty fact.

Being over knee deep in water, Billy perfectly completed an electrical circuit that would have made Mr. Edison very proud of his new invention. To avoid the obvious pain to the electrical contact points, our cowboy-turned-fisherman pushed down on the metal conduit to clear the wire from his crotch, now sending the jolting electricity up through his arms and back down his body to complete the electrical circuit.

149

I'm sure you get the picture. There's an old sayin' about "Bein' danged if you do and danged if you don't." That probably fits this frantic scene about as well as any ever will. Push down on the conduit, to relieve the pain only to get a shock in a different place ... let up on the conduit and get another crotch jolt. "Danged if you do and danged if you don't."

The next several seconds probably seemed like a week to poor ol' Billy. It's really too bad it wasn't after dark and that there was no photographer present to capture the phenomenon for posterity. I'm sure our now very sober cowboy was going on and off like the neon sign on the Stockman Bar.

Before it was over, Billy nearly drowned and tore out at least a quarter of a mile of fence, but by golly Dick was right. He DID get a big charge out of salmon fishin'.

"I jus' wisht I'da had one o' them movie cameras. Yer nose was goin' on 'n off jus' like the sign on the Stockman Bar."

Chapter Twenty Nine

My X Rated Granny

I've got to be one of the luckiest guys alive. I had a great childhood. I know it isn't really all that uncommon for a country kid to have grown up with their Grandparents right in the same yard, but I feel sorry for all the kids that didn't have that opportunity. They've really missed something.

Of course it didn't hurt anything that I was the oldest, smartest, and most handsome-est of the grandkids. I really had a good thing going. The milk tasted a lot better at Granny's house (although it came out of the same cow as the milk at Mom and Dad's) and the popcorn was a lot better, too.

It was sort of like having two sets of parents, except that Grandad and Granny were a lot more fun. They took the time to teach me to play checkers and card games and all the fun things that Dads and Moms sometimes get too busy to do.

Granny didn't always go by the name Granny. She was just Grandma until way up in the sixties sometime after I was grown. When the *Beverly Hillbillies* came on TV the name change was inevitable. The old lady that played Granny Clampett on that program was a dead ringer for my Grandma Overcast, so Granny she was from then on. My Granny was a gen-u-ine hillbilly from the Ozarks and ever' bit as spry and resourceful as Granny Clampett. They both had that folksy southern twang in their voice and they even looked a little alike.

When the cook and I tied the knot, my Grandparents bought a house in town and a motor home to go fishin' in. I thought at the time it was because they wanted to slow down and enjoy life a little, but to tell you the truth, I think the real reason was to just make room for us.

Of course having raised a family in the midst of the Great Depression, they were always pretty close with their money. They also had the decent moral standards common to folks of that era and lived what they believed. If you could pick a perfect Grandad and Granny, they'd be it.

Along in the seventies sometime, my Grandad developed some kind of health problems and had to have several outpatient treatments at the hospital in Great Falls. Because they had their motor home, a place to stay wasn't an issue. They just pulled into a campground in town and set up housekeeping.

Here they were in a big city (at least by country standards) with extra time on their hands, and after a few days decided they'd like to take in a movie. It had been years since they'd seen one. Unfortunately, that was about the time that the decency factor in movies took a turn to the south. Compared to what's shown in movie houses nowadays, they were probably pretty tame, but these folks were used to shows like "Ma and Pa Kettle Go to Town."

The motion picture industry had just recently developed the rating system. The buzz down at the Senior Citizens Center was all about how terrible some of the modern movies were, and Grandad and Granny had been hearing wild horror stories. To make sure that they didn't go to a naughty movie, they were paying special attention to the ratings. They looked all over town for a G ... no luck. Then they looked for a PG ... nope there wasn't one of those playing either. All of the movies playing were either rated R or X. There was quite a lively discussion about which one of the ratings would be the least nasty.

"We sure don't want to go to an R rated show," Granny stated emphatically. "R means that they're actually restricting kids right at the door. That must be a terrible one."

"Yea, I think you're right," Grandad chimed in. I guess we better go to the X Rated one."

So that's what they did, and it was awful.

Merely trying to conjure up a mental picture of my eighties-something grandparents in an X Rated movie is difficult. The opening scene was enough to make a sailor blush and it went downhill from there. I'm sure Granny was on the edge of her seat with both hands tightly clutching the handle of the purse in her lap.

"Dad! Would you look at that! Just imagine how bad those R Rated ones must be! I can't watch this! Let's go!"

Karleen & Dow Overcast, Sr. in 1980
"Grandad & Granny"
(Can YOU envision them in an X rated movie?)

Here's where the penny pinching, Depression Survivor mentality clashed with the morally upright church goin' Family Patriarch. The penny pincher won.

"No! We're not leavin'. I paid ten bucks to get us in here, and we're a gonna watch it."

By George, they did too.

Chapter Thirty

Isabell.... One Tough Female

This is an incredibly true story of Isabell. A tale of one extraordinary female's struggle along life's sometimes crooked, and in this case, very perilous pathway. Life isn't always fair, and Isabell found herself repeatedly thrust literally into the jaws of death. It's a true story of survival against all odds, yet a story who's final chapter yet remains a mystery.

I never had the opportunity to meet Isabell or to ask her any of the details of her experiences personally. It's probably just as well. Because of a language barrier, I doubt if I could have understood her anyway. English wasn't her first language ... actually it wasn't even her second, and she was even less proficient in English than I am in Spanish, her second language. (And that ain't sayin' very much).

Isabell came from a very large family in southern Arizona down near the Mexican border. That's the reason for her inclination towards Spanish. She was of mixed blood decent. Her Mama MIGHT have been from Rhode Island, and her Daddy's roots were probably in Mexico. This is only speculation on my part, and the reason for my supposing that Spanish was probably her second language.

Her smattering of red feathers gave away her Rhode Island Red heritage, and geography her Mexican connection. Her first language being some sort of "Chickenese," gave her a very limited understanding of Spanish, and absolutely none whatsoever of English. As I mentioned previously, a personal visit probably wouldn't have revealed much that I could understand anyway. This story is pieced together from several eye witness accounts, and is as factual as I can possibly make it ... incredible as it may sound.

That fateful day back in the 1990's began just like all of the others. Isabell was just leisurely strolling across the ranch yard peckin' the undigested kernels of grain from the smattering of fresh cow pies. A couple of the guys that owned the place were walking past. That's when disaster struck and this long and unfortunate chain of events began. Life is sort of like that, isn't it? It doesn't matter if you happen to be a human bein' or a chicken, the fickle finger of fate sometimes reaches out and gives you a poke; even if you're just mindin' your own business.

The boys were headed up in their Cessna to check the cattle in one of the remote pastures. "It ain't fair, Jack."

"What ain't fair?"

"Dang, I love flyin'. I'd a lot rather fly than walk, an' there goes a dumb chicken that would rather walk than fly ... an' she's got wings an' ever'thing."

"She ain't flyin' 'cause she CAN'T, you dummy. Them wings are just fer show."

"I betcha she can ... let's just take her with us and find out for sure."

It's probably fortunate that Isabell was raised by the Ramirez family and didn't understand a word

156

they said. Before she even knew what happened, she found herself imprisoned in a cardboard box ... 5,000 feet above the bakin' Arizona desert. The cattle had been checked and it was time for the villainous experiment; ... can a chicken really fly if given the proper amount of incentive and altitude?

Details of Isabell's 5,000 foot trip back to earth are sketchy. One of the kidnapers testified that the plane circled the desperately flapping hen until they saw her land on the ground with a thump of feathers and stagger off into the desert.

"See I tol' ya she'd make it. You owe me ten bucks! Chickens CAN fly if they want to!"

As traumatic as that chapter of Isabell's life was, her troubles were just beginning. She now found herself disoriented from the crash landin' and lost in the 110 degree plus desert; no map, no canteen, and no lunch. After hours of aimless wandering in the blistering heat she stumbled across a fairly well traveled road.

This was by no means a sure sign of salvation. In the first place it's hard for a chicken (with no thumbs) to hitch a ride, and in the second place, she'd lost so many feathers in the landing that any passerby would hesitate to stop for someone as disheveled looking as she was.

Fortunately, Louie stopped. Louie was a kind hearted man. He tenderly lifted her nearly lifeless body into the cab of the pickup and coaxed a little water down her parched throat. He was scheduled to eat dinner with the Wilson's and upon arriving informed Kristy, the cook, that he had a present for her.

"A chicken?!?" Kristy exclaimed. "Where in the world did you get a chicken?"

Although Louie was a Mexican and Isabell probably understood his soothing Spanish perfectly, she was at a loss to communicate her harrowing flight. All Louie knew was where he found her. Why she was there was still at that point a mystery. The ranch house bustled with the activity of dinner and Isabell was placed outside in the shade with a little feed and temporarily forgotten.

"I've gotta run into town for parts. Wanna ride along?" Dave Wilson asked his bride.

"Sure," Kristi grinned, "let's go."

It was about twenty five bumpy country road miles into town, and it was haying time so the Wilson's wasted no time.... there was lots of haying to do. They hurried to the parts house, and then went to a gas station to fill up their old four wheel drive before they started the long bouncing trip home.

"Hey, what's that on the rear end of yer pickup?" the guy behind them at the gas station yelled. The Wilsons checked and sure enough, there she was.... it was Isabell hanging on to the rear differential for dear life.

"It's that crazy chicken that Louie picked up! How in the dickens did she ride all the way in here on the rear end of the pickup without falling off?"

"I dunno ... I guess she'll get off when she's ready."

With that the Wilson's headed back to the ranch. Twenty five bumpy miles later, Isabell was still there, her little chicky feet locked in a death grip on the rear differential. They went to the hay field, and when they returned later in the day, Isabel was gone and no one has seen her since.

She didn't say goodbye or even leave a note. Isabell's final fate is just speculation. She probably hoofed it for home. Whether or not she ever it made remains a mystery. She more than likely wound up as lunch for one of the desert's jillion rattlesnakes or maybe as the main course in a hungry wetback's pot.

Nope.... life ain't always fair. All I know is after all Isabell had been through ... she dang shore DESERVED to make it.

158

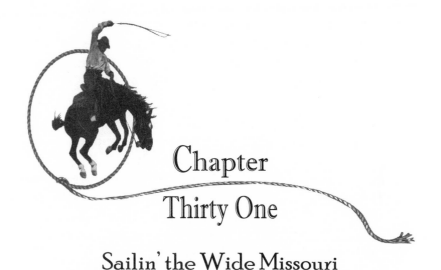

Chapter
Thirty One

Sailin' the Wide Missouri

$\mathcal{T}$ime has a way of changing everything. We're all a bunch of marshmallows compared to the normal modus-operande of our counter parts from a generation or two ago. There are quite a few stunts that the ol' boys used to pull as a matter of routine that would make us pampered modern day cowboys look like a bunch of sissies. Here's a good example:

It was the spring of '45 or '46. There was a young fella that I'll call Larry. (He's the only one from this little tale still alive.) The big War was just over and Larry had gotten one of those Willys Jeeps. It would follow any wagon trail in the Bear Paws, so one warm spring morning he took off on one of them. This one led north from their place on the head of Eagle Creek by the foot of Ol' Baldy, onto the Indian Reservation and then over the divide to Johnny Phalen's.

That's quite a trip. There's not a prettier piece of real estate in the whole world. I think the Good

Lord made that part of the country last ... after He'd practiced up a little on some of the rest of it.

As luck would have it Gregory "Buck" Henderson was at Phalen's that day. He and the Phalens went way back. Johnny's dad, Ambrose, was one of the earliest white settlers in that part of the country and Buck had started roping calves at their brandin's when he was still knee high to a grasshopper.

Buck and Johnny were in the process of loading up a dry cow in the back of an old three quarter ton International pickup. The plan was to haul her to the auction in Lewistown and then stay overnight for the bull sale the next day. When invited along, Larry jumped at the chance. He'd never been to any exotic places like London or Paris or Lewistown.

Down the cow trail that substituted for a road the three Bear Paw adventurers rattled. Larry had never crossed the Missouri River before, but he knew there was a ferry down there someplace. What he didn't know was there WASN'T one south of beautiful downtown Warrick, Montana.

Just getting to the river down through the breaks was an experience. That crooked steep trail was enough to make a billy goat blush. When they at long last reached the river, there was no ferry in sight. Buck crawled out of the pickup and began walkin' up and down the bank.

He said he was "lookin' fer sign." It wasn't until then that Larry got the picture. Those guys must be nuts. They're actually going to DRIVE that pickup across the Missouri River?

"Ah, as soon as the ice goes off it's a purty good crossin' here if the water ain't too high," Buck assured him. "We'll make 'er alright."

Buck Henderson Heelin' Calves in '99

Buck found whatever sign he was lookin' for in the mud along the bank, and headed back to the pickup. He and Johnny each took a big swig from the whiskey jug they had stashed behind the seat to properly christen their upcoming voyage.

Not being a drinker himself Larry declined, but as the pickup eased off into the chilly muddy water he was wondering to himself if he'd made a couple of big mistakes; the first was coming along with these two characters, and the second was turning down their offer of liquid courage.

Being in the middle of the Missouri River in a pickup with a dry cow in the back, accompanied by two crazy guys that are drinkin', can be a little nerve wracking for a fella that can't swim. Larry was scared spitless. There was nothing but a wagon track on the far bank to aim for, but apparently they made all of the right guesses. They pulled out on the other side easy as you please.

"Told ja we'd make 'er," Buck scoffed, taking another pull off the jug to commemorate their successful cruise.

They made it to Lewistown and sold the cow ... yet another reason to celebrate. The next morning the boys poured themselves out of their bunks and headed for the bull sale. Johnny wound up with a huge roan Durham bull that they could barely stuff in the back of the pickup, and with a fresh jug for the road, back for the Bear Paws they headed.

The river didn't look any better to Larry now than it did the first time. The whiskey sure did. Although he again declined, he was beginning to see the possible benefits of impaired thinking. A clouded mind might actually make drowning appear less sinister.

The heavy bull gave the old pickup plenty of traction and helped to hold the radiator fan at least partly out of the water. All was going well until the back end of the outfit went down and there they were ... stuck. The roan bull was bellerin' and thrashin' around in the back. He was just as scared as Larry was ... and mad to boot.

162

"Well," Johnny pondered, thoughtfully contemplating their predicament. "Don't count us out yet. We still got a rope. I'll tie one end on the front bumper with a slip knot, an' you go put the loop aroun' the bulls horns. Then let him out an' fan him around the front end for the bank. He'll pull us right out."

"Dad Blame it, Buck......
I think we lost 'im."

To a fella that wasn't drinkin' this DID look like a hair brained idea, but they were only about twenty yards from the far bank, and their options were sort of limited. It looked like their only shot. Unfortunately, they forgot to let the bull in on this brilliant flash of inspiration, and a bonehead monkeyin' around with his horns was simply more than his temper could take. Before the boys could get their rope on him, out over the top of the starboard listing stock rack he went.

It was probably just as well. O' Roany headed back across the river towards Lewistown on a high lope.... with water splashin' twenty feet in the air. The boys were still stuck, and their only hope was quickly out of sight over the ridge on the south side of the river. I don't know if they ever found him again or not.

The Missouri Breaks can be lonesome country, but the feeling of being stranded in the middle of the river in a bogged down pickup with water running through it is one that most of us can barely comprehend. They weren't exactly on a well traveled through-fare.

They say the Lord looks out for children and idiots. These boys weren't exactly kids anymore, but they apparently fit sufficiently into the second category. Guess what? Before long they spied a team and wagon coming down the steep trail into the river bottom.

"Hey, that's Bud Corrigan," Buck remarked with a glimmer of hope. "We might not drown after all."

Bud unhitched his team and rode one of the horses out to the stranded sailors.

"You boys got a problem?" Bud chuckled. "I got a new roll o' barb wire. If one o' you guys 'll get on behind me, we can twist a little of it together an' maybe getcha out of this pickle."

Larry was quick to volunteer. If that whiskey bottle hadn't been empty, it was beginning to look better all the time. They stretched out three long strands of wire, twisted it together, and tied it on to the front axle. Bud's team pulled them out with their makeshift tow rope as slick as you please.

"See ...," Buck said to his tenderfoot travelin' partner. "I tol' ja we'd make 'er."

Chapter
Thirty Two

Still Hangin' On

I think it was at a Fourth of July picnic back in the early fifties when this little tale originated. There was a community get together in the Bear Paw Mountains. The exact location has been clouded by time, but that really isn't important anyway.

It was the kind of old fashioned celebration that communities all over the West used to enjoy before progress messed everything up. There were the foot races, the sack races, and the huge supplies of watermelon and homemade ice cream. The ladies always outdid themselves and brought only their very best recipes.

Of course none of them will ever admit it, but community potlucks are really only thinly disguised cooking contests. The dish that gets finished off first is the one that obviously belongs to the community's best cook, and the competition is fierce.

The men, on the other hand, might have thrown a few horseshoes, but their main source of entertainment came from gathering around an old water trough filled with ice and refreshments. In no time, the stories would begin to roll. Some folks maintain that there is direct correlation between the length of time the boys sat around that water trough and the entertainment value of the yarns being spun. If the volume level of the laughter is a reliable indication, they must be right.

I wasn't there, and if I had been, I'd probably have been too young and way too busy damming up the creek or climbin' a mountain to stick around to listen to those crusty old timers weave tale after tale. Boy, what I wouldn't give for that opportunity now.

This is how the story got passed down to me. Russell Olson was one of the old timers present that warm Fourth of July so many years ago. He loved to recount this story. It's too bad he's not with us anymore, so we could appreciate it all over again. He'd laugh so hard that he'd cry, and you could hear him for a half a mile. Dan Murphy, Bill Young, Steve Boyce, Leonard Faber, and Joe Kinsella were some of the ol' boys that he mentioned were there.

As the stories went around the circle, Bill Felton was the next to speak up. He gotten a black horse in a trade that was bad to buck, and he was wavin' his arms and telling the wild tale of getting on him one cold morning the spring before.

"I could see by that white eyeball of his and that six inches of slack between the rear end of the saddle and his back I was pro'bly in for it. So I cheeked him around real hard when I stepped on, an' I'll be doggoned if he didn't stand there still as a statue, so

166

I jus' turned him loose t' let him step on out. Boys, that's when all hell busted loose!"

Ol' Bill's arms really got to flappin' now as he described the wild chain of events to follow. "I never seen a horse buck that hard in my whole life. I swear t' Goo'ness he must o' went ten feet straight up. I grabbed a hold fer all I was worth. B'fore he even hit the groun' he was headed the other way with his front feet stuck right in the bit ... an' I was still hangin' on fer dear life."

Bill Felton & Baldy in the 50's

There's nothin' that will excite a bunch of ol' cowboys like the story of a good buckin' horse ride, so he had everyone's complete attention. A couple of the boys reached back into the icy water trough for a fresh bottle of what ever was in there, and urged him to finish his story.

"Then what happened?" one of the boys asked. "What happened next?"

"We'll I's still hangin' on, but you should o' seen that bugger buck," Bill continued, taking a long draw from the cold brew in his hand before he continued.

"By the third jump he'd plumb shed the saddle blanket. Bucked 'er right out from under the saddle ... but I was still hangin' on." The boys knew Bill was a good hand with a horse, but this really WAS a bad one.

"A couple more jumps an' he'd shucked the whole outfit, saddle and all. Bucked it plumb off ... but there I was still hangin' on." There was a long pregnant silence as ol' Bill squinted one eye at his audience and waited for their reaction.

"Doggone it, Bill," one of the boys finally asked. If he bucked the whole outfit off, what was you hangin' on TO?"

Moments like that are ones that a true storyteller likes to savor ... to milk for all that they're worth. He was just WAITIN' for someone to ask. After just the proper amount of stallin' to get the maximum effect from a durn good story, Bill squinted his eye again and screwed the lid on it.

"What was I hangin' on to?" Bill roared, "Heck, I was hangin' on to a quakin' asp limb about ten feet off the ground. He lost me on the first jump!"

Chapter Thirty Three

Darcie's Fresh Start

*L*ife isn't always fair. In fact, it rarely is if a fella stops to think about it. It isn't too hard for any of us to think about someone that has had every opportunity in the world to succeed, and through bad choices or poor management, or just plain ol' stupidity has tinkled it all against the fence.

But then, hard times aren't all bad. That's the reason that the new immigrants to this country do so well. They know what having it tough really is. They'll come and live two or three families of them in one house, and about twenty of them go and get a couple of minimum wage jobs apiece and pool their money, and before you know it, they're buying a skyscraper in downtown LA. We fat, spoiled Americans would never think of living like that. We have opportunity everywhere we look, but for some reason are blind to most of it.

Not only is life not fair, but growin' up is tough these days. There are kids that take a wrong turn and break the old folks' hearts, and then there are

169

Moms and Dads that screw up and make life a lot harder for their young'uns than it needs to be. No matter what age you happen to be when you mess up, most of the time it's that same old tangled up thinkin'; that the grass is greener on the other side of the fence. It hardly ever is.

Sometimes out of the pain caused by someone takin' the wrong trail there's a little glimmer of hope if you look hard enough. "It's an ill wind that blows no good." Once in a while we get a chance to hear a story that just sort of warms your heart, and makes you feel good down deep inside, like a big deep breath of fresh Spring air first thing in the morning.

This is a story like that. It's a true story that's still unfolding as I write this. I've taken the liberty of changing the names. The reason for that is simple. It's not really my story to tell. That right belongs to the main characters. It's their story. I think you'll see what I mean.

There's a gal (we'll call her Darcie) that's getting a second chance after going through some tough times that were no fault of her own, and there's an old cowboy (we'll call him Barry) that's giving it to her after going down a rough trail himself.

It all started late last Fall when a friend of mine we'll call Keith was driving down a lonesome stretch of highway out here in the West. He'd been behind the wheel for several hours, had a few more to go, and needed to stretch his legs a little, so he pulled off at a little roadside tavern.

It was just a friendly little country place, but was nearly empty. Down near the end of the bar sat Barry alone. Now Keith is a cowboy, so it wasn't hard for him to tell with one eyeball that the weathered old codger sitting there alone would be the sort of a guy he'd enjoy visitin' with.

Bein' a sociable rascal, and always enjoying a little conversation with someone that knew the difference between a horse and a cow, Keith sat down beside the ol' guy and ordered them both a drink. After they introduced themselves and visited about the weather some, Barry mentioned that maybe he recognized Keith's last name.

"You any relation to that gal that barrel races?"

"Yea," Keith answered, trying to not let his pride show too much, "that's my daughter." Barry got a lonesome sort of a look in his eye, that seemed a little hard to figure, but Keith went on explaining a few of the shows they'd been to lately, and how his little girl was doing. He swore he thought he noticed a little tear in the corner of the old cowboy's eye, but naw.... that couldn't be.

After a little pause in the conversation it was Barry's turn. "I was hopin' to get my granddaughter mounted so's she could win a few of those. I bought her a couple of real well bred barrel prospects and a brand new saddle, but...." The old cowboy's words just sort of quit comin' and it was plain now that those WERE tears in his eyes.

The ol' boy swallowed hard a couple of times and went on. "....reckon it wasn't meant to be. I found that new saddle in a pawn shop last summer, and had to buy it all over again. That little girl o' mine got in with the wrong crowd.... Heaven knows what's gonna happen to her, but here I am with a brand new thirteen inch saddle with a nice deep seat and a couple of good barrel prospects, and ... " his words just trailed off again. He pulled out an old red 'kerchief from his overalls and blew his nose, and there was a long painful silence.

That's a mighty uncomfortable place to find yourself. It's almost like hearing something that you're not supposed to hear and seeing something that your eyes don't have any business seein'.

After what seemed like a lifetime, Keith spoke up again. "Life just ain't fair." That's when he told Barry about Darcie. It seems her Ma had run off out of state lookin' for greener pastures, and had left the

171

little gal with her Pa. What was maybe even worse than that, was before she left, she'd up and sold the saddle that Darcie had claimed and the horse she was learnin' to run the barrels on.

"That little snip is only 'leven years old, but she sticks to the back of a horse like a bur," Keith continued. "Life ain't fair, I tell, ya. She's been ridin' barrel horses that belong to the older girls over our way ever' chance she gets. Boy, what a hand."

" ... and then her mother has to run off and wreck everything ... wonder what that durn woman was thinkin', anyway? It dang shore took the wind out of that little girl's sails, I know that."

"Don't tell me no more," Barry blubbered. "You'll have me bawlin' for sure."

Though Keith had places to go and things to do, right now nothing seemed quite as important as finishing the conversation with his broken hearted new friend. They spent quite a little time there that day with Barry finally getting a handle on his sniffles, and eventually having the courage to inquire more about little Darcie and the rotten hand that life had dealt her.

The final chapter of this little story is yet to be written. Both Barry's granddaughter and Darcie's Mom have taken trails that have broken the hearts of those that love them the most. Just how all that plays out is really hard to tell, but the last words that Barry echoed as Keith went out the door that day are sure to rub a little salve on at least two broken hearts, and will go a long ways in encouraging the rest of us that sometimes sad stories actually do have happy endings.

"Here's my phone number. Now, I mean what I said before. You just bring that little girl back over here. I've got two good papered colts and a new barrel saddle, and they're hers if she wants 'em."

Just maybe life IS fair after all. 🔪

Chapter

Thirty Four

Fearless Frank

Curlews can have a real bad attitude. I learned that fact several years ago, but I've never been in a scrape as bad as my brother Frank got into not long ago. Curlews are those birds with skinny little legs and a long curved beak that sort of droops down on the end.

They're fairly common around here and since I had my run in with them back in the 70's sometime, I've made a wide circle around 'em. I'm even going to be more wary of the little buggers from now on.

My bad experience came while I was cutting hay on an old open topped swather. I don't know if I ran over their nest or if they were just having a bad day, but all of a sudden I had a couple of them dive bombin' me with their mouths open. I'll tell you what, when they're coming at you from all directions, and you're trying to swat them off and keep the machinery all running straight at the same time, things get sort of hectic. That big old open beak full of sharp teeth looks even bigger when it's zeroed in on you.

My choice for a weapon of defense left quite a little to be desired. After all, I was out there to cut hay, not defend myself. I think an old oil jug was all I could scrape up under the circumstances, and was wildly swinging it over my head in a desperate attempt to keep from becoming a curlew hors d'oeuvre. They finally gave up, but not before giving me a real scare.

Frank's day started off great. It had rained, and he had the time so he loaded up his horse and rattled his trailer to the summer field to check the bulls he'd scattered a few days before. Things turned sour right off the bat. First, he found a couple of dead critters. Who knows what killed them, but here was a cow and calf with their feet in the air. Next he found a couple of bulls that had gone haywire and needed replacing. It's funny how a smile that the rain puts on a fella's face can be so easily wiped off in a heart beat.

Unfortunately, his bull field was empty. There weren't any spares left, and he needed a couple more, NOW. That time of year, the bull shippers that have good bulls to sell are getting their herds pretty well picked over, and the good ones are all sold. But then, when you need one bad, even a not-so-good bull is better than none at all.

That's when Frank's luck took a turn for the better (briefly). He's bought several bulls from Larry and Patty Nissen, so he gave them a call. As luck would have it, they had a pretty good yearlin' bull that had frozen his ears when he was born, so they had kept him out of their sale. (I really doubt if an amorous cow will even notice his short ears, and if he somehow happens to figure out how to transmit the stubby ears to his off-spring it'd be the first time in history.) The Nissens also had a herd bull they didn't need that they agreed to lease. Frank was back in the saddle again.

Fearless Frank doing what he does best. Eatin' MY groceries.

"What if somethin' happens to your herd bull while he's at my place? With the luck I'm havin' something will probably go wrong with him, too," he asks Larry as they're loading up. "You s'pose I should insure him?"

"Naw. Don't worry about it. He'll probably be OK. If something happens to him ... well that's just the way it goes. We're not going to be needing him anymore this year, so go ahead and use him."

Frank tends to be a little on the excitable side anyway, and horrifying thoughts of Nissen's high priced herd bull going bad while he's in with his cows were bouncing around in his pointed little head as he slid the trailer and its precious cargo down the slimy gumbo road. It was the middle of the afternoon by now, and a nearly perfect day, even though the road was pretty slick. Frank had his window down enjoying the fresh smell that only a good rain on sagebrush can produce when he first noticed the curlew.

It was flying right beside his pickup not ten feet from the driver's door and about eyeball level. That seemed a little strange. It also seemed a little odd that the crazy bird would squint his eyes and look right at him with a menacing snarl on his beak. Thirty miles an hour, neck in neck down the country road they went. Once in a while the bird would go right in front of the pickup and drop down completely out of sight, only to swoop up and circle around again and glare with those little beady eyes of his into Frank's open window.

The second or third time he swooped in front of the outfit and down out of the line of sight, Frank was worried that he'd run over him so he honked his horn. Maybe curlews don't like the sound of a pickup horn.

"He was tryin' to peck me to death!
An' I'm tryin' to get ahold of my pistol!"

This time he circled around again, and WHOOSH came right in the pickup window with his mouth open and murder on his mind! I'm tellin' you, those birds are nuts.

He wound up on the back of the seat behind Frank, peckin' the dickens out of the back of his head with that long dagger-like beak and trying to flop him to

177

death with his wings. I told you Frank was a little excitable, remember? He's trying desperately to hold the pickup and trailer on the narrow slippery gumbo road by steering with his knees while simultaneously fending off a carnivorous, deranged bird with one hand and reaching under the seat for his pistol with the other.

Thank God he couldn't get his hands on that pistol. I can just imagine the cab full of bullet holes, not to mention trying to shoot a bird that's eatin' on the back of your head. When the pickup and trailer finally came to a stop, it was perched precariously on the edge of the slippery road with the curlew still flopping and nibblin' on the driver. At least Nissen's high-priced herd bull was still in one piece.

Frank threw open the door and the deranged bird flew off for parts unknown, hopefully to never return. The entire episode did no real harm, except to permanently and irreparably damage the reputation of the heretofore "Fearless Frank".

"Fearless Frank" had wet his pants.

Chapter Thirty Five

Mama's Snakey Basement

*W*e just had another snake in our basement. Although there wasn't any real harm done ... except to the snake and the nerves of my poor little cook who happened to step in the middle of him on the stairs, the incident has provided not only fodder for another sordid tale of the misadventures on our ramshackle outfit, but also a little glimpse into human nature and what makes different people tick.

I'll be doggoned if I know how they're gettin' in, but we've wound up with four or five snakes in the house through the years. No rattlers, thank God. This was a nice big bull snake about four feet long, and was dispatched by my brother "Fearless Frank" (of Curlew-in-his-pickup fame). It happened sort of like this:

Fearless Frank was here to bum dinner ... by default, we're sort of on his grub line. My little cook was headed down in the basement to rustle up an

179

extra tater, and Frank was lounging in the rockin' chair with his back to the basement door. The second step down, Cookie steps in the middle of Mr. Snake (about as big around as a can of corn), who is trying his best to mind his own business and take a little nap on the stairs.

Both the stepper and the stepee were equally startled by this unplanned confrontation. The head and tail ends of Mr. Snake shot up in the air as a result of 95 pounds worth of solid muscle mass and gristle standing on his tummy, and the cook shrieked and grabbed the first available handhold (Fearless Frank's hair).

She somehow managed to simultaneously soar two stairs straight up and three feet straight back. Although since the incident she's been bragging of her extreme physical prowess, I think that handful of hair had a lot to do with it. She dang near broke poor ol' Frank's neck. (That oughta teach him to ride the grub line.)

This last snake was nearly as big as the one that visited a couple of years ago. That one was a real honker. Again it was a bull snake, and I (again) was conveniently not around to rescue my little damsel in distress.

Lawrence and Sheri Miller were doing some haying for us that year, and that's who Dawn called for help. Keeping one wary eye on the snake, she dialed up the neighbors.

"Sheri, this is Dawn. I've got a snake on my step and Kenny's gone, and I need Lawrence to come over right away!"

"Is it a rattlesnake?"

"I don't know ... I can't tell, but he's on my steps!"

"Lawrence went to town for parts, and he should be home any minute. I'll tell him when he gets home," Sheri answered calmly.

Dawn hung up the phone, and then got to thinking that "excitable" Sheri didn't seem as concerned as maybe she should have, so she called her back, and Sheri answered again.

"I called around looking for Lawrence, but couldn't catch him. If you've got a snake on the step, why don't you just go get a shovel and kill 'im?" she questioned.

"I didn't think you sounded excited enough! I can't take my eye off him that's why! He's on my basement steps, and I don't want to lose him! If he was on the outside steps I wouldn't have bothered you! He's in my HOUSE ... on the BASEMENT STEPS!"

A blood curdling shriek literally leaped from the nearly melted the telephone receiver.

THAT'S the reaction that can be expected from Sheri Miller when she's excited about something. "For cryin' out loud! A snake?!? In your HOUSE?!? Don't take your eyes off him! I'll get my pistol and be right over!

Sheri and I have played a lot of music together through the years, and there isn't anyone (male or female) I'd rather have on my side in a scrap ... but ... a confrontation between an excitable 44 Magnum pistol packin' Sheri Miller and a snake in my cement basement is not an image that conjures up any comforting thoughts.

Thank God, Lawrence drove in the yard just as she was leaving with pistol in hand. He drove right down here and took care of the snake. It takes very little imagination to see bullet holes in everything in the basement, including Sheri Miller and my hot water tank. The doggone bullets would still be ricocheting around those concrete walls.

But, I'm sorry ... I've digressed from this most recent snake story, and its hero "Fearless Frank." Eager to reclaim his rightful name, "Fearless" bravely descended the stairs into the snake pit (shaking knees and all), armed only with a measly hoe.

"Where in the dickens is Sheri Miller and her pistol when you REALLY need her?" he was almost fearlessly thinking.

He found Mr. Snake wrapped around a water pipe near the basement ceiling, and after an unrepeatable expletive or two, jerked down his doomed victim and sent him to wherever snakes that scare the pants off people go when they die.

Our basement floor will never be the same. It's got hacky little hoe marks all over it that will take at least a gallon of that putty stuff to fix. But this time ... Frank did indeed live up to his "Fearless" reputation.

... this time ... "Fearless Frank" DIDN'T wet his pants.

Chapter Thirty Six

Billy & The Big Cat

*T*here was a near tragedy in Dick 'n Billy's camp not long ago. There's been a big cat in that neck of the woods for a while, and it's got a lot of folks on edge.

Mountain lions have a pretty wide range so they tell me. Seeing one once in a while is sort of a novelty, but there have been more frequent sightings in that area lately, and there's some concern that a couple of them may have denned up. One of them got into a herd of horses just over the hill from there early this summer and killed several head, and messed up a few more of them so bad they had to be disposed of.

They've got a scream that will make the hair on the back of your neck stand up. It sorta sounds like a really BIG woman in pain and on steroids. The first time Billy heard it, the boys were gathering yearlin's down near where Skunk Creek dumps into the Missouri River. It nearly scared him to death.

He was about as nervous as a fella could be, looking over his shoulder and in every tree and around every rock until he got back to the trailer. Dick had just ridden up a minute or two before.

"You hear that mountain lion?" Billy stammered.

"Nope ... what mountain lion?"

"I heard one in the brush about a mile or so down the creek. I'll tell you what, I never wished I was packin' a gun so bad in my life," Billy sputtered, just thankful to be back at the outfit in one piece.

"Yer kiddin'. I never heard no mountain lion," Dick countered.

"I can't believe you didn't hear it. You was just over a ridge or two. It was right down there on the south side where that hog back ridge comes down to the creek."

Thank goodness the boys hadn't lost any livestock; at least they didn't find any remains. A couple of days later they were getting loaded up to head down that way again.

"I sure do feel tough again today," Dick grumped as he saddled Ol' Yeller, a big palomino four-year-old he'd been riding. "My head feels big as a washtub, an' this nose o' mine is runnin' like a garden hose."

"It's purty early in the year for shippin' fever," Billy quipped. " ... 'sides I'll betcha you live through it. I'll tell you what though, I'm takin' a gun down there this time," he continued as he strapped a scabbard on his saddle. "That durn cat ain't gonna catch me flat footed again, that's fer sure. What you got that ol' chunk o' hay rope for?"

Dick was tying a loop in the end of a length of old fat hay rope. "This durn colt is pretty rope shy around his legs, an' I don't want to wear out my good lariat draggin' it around in the rocks. I think I'll jus' let him drag this one around today," Dick sniffled.

The boys got their horses in the trailer and rattled down the gumbo trail several miles to the field on the creek they were going to ride again, searching for any yearlin's they might have missed.

"Why don't you ride down the north side, and check the breaks out over there," Billy suggested, "an' I'll take the ridge on the south side. Maybe I might even see that cat this time. I'll meet you down at the hogback."

Dick mumbled something about not feeling much like ridin' today, and headed off towards the north end of the field with twenty feet of hay rope draggin' from his saddle horn. Billy jammed his Winchester into its scabbard and struck a lope towards the south, keeping his eyes and ears tuned for any lion sign. He tends to be a little on the spooky side anyway, and the big cat really had his nerves on edge.

The ride was pretty uneventful, with neither of the boys catching sight of missing cattle or roving mountain lions. Billy made it back to the rendezvous point first, and removing his rifle from the scabbard ... just in case ... settled down with his back propped against a rock to wait for his partner. It was about mid morning, and the area there near the creek was pretty thick with brush.

That's when he heard it again! That high pitched scream he'd heard a couple of days before ... the cat was back, and this time it was even closer than before! Billy quietly levered a round into the chamber on his 30-30 and anxiously scanned the brush in the direction he'd heard the cat. Suddenly he caught a glimpse of the cat's tail and a flash of its tawny coat passing between two clumps of the thick brush not thirty yards away. He could hear the faint crunching sound as the animal stealthily made its way through the thick growth.

From the direction it was headed, Billy was certain it would emerge in a small clearing just a few feet ahead. He leveled the old Winchester at the edge of the clearing and took careful aim.... just waiting for the cat to appear and the opportunity to squeeze off a shot.

IT appeared alright, but thank goodness he'd waited for a clear shot. It was just Dick ... ridin' a yellow horse and draggin' a chunk of yellow hay rope. He hadn't even seen his pardner yet, so didn't know just how close he'd come to being shot. He stopped in the middle of the clearing, and there was the same unmistakably chilling sound Billy had heard before.

With a big red farmer 'kerchief ... Dick was blowin' his nose.

"Yea, that's the closest I ever come to
shootin' you, Dick. An' that time
you never even had it comin'."

186

Chapter Thirty Seven

Ridin' For Fancy Pants

*T*rey and his partner Vic used to ride together some years ago. They had hired on at one of those fancy-pants outfits in Texas. The guy that owned the ranch had big bucks, and didn't even know which end of a cow got up first. But ... he paid pretty well, and his checks always cleared the bank, so it was a lot better place to work than some of the others they'd tried.

The boss wanted to be a cowboy ... well, sort of, but his was more the Hollywood version than the real deal, and when you're loaded, I guess you just do things the way YOU want to do 'em. I don't have a clue where he got all that money, but there were a couple of pretty good reasons why everyone knew it wasn't ranchin'.

First, he didn't know sick 'um about cows, and second, he actually HAD money. The best way to wind up a millionaire ranchin' really hasn't changed much through the years. All you have to do is have two million before you start.

It wasn't all that big an outfit; they just ran a few hundred head of cows, and they had some of the best horseflesh that money could buy. "Fancy Pants" (the nickname they gave him behind his back) wasn't even there most of the time. He had an old Mexican by the name of Gonzalo that took care of the chores and the buildings, so the boys just pretty much had the run of the outfit, and kept the cattle where they needed to be on good feed and water. That was even easier that normal ... another advantage of not having any mortgage payments to meet ... because the outfit was only about half stocked, so there was grass to burn.

One afternoon in May, the big-shot boss and a couple of his crony pals came cruisin' into the yard in his big white Caddy. Of course, the entire crew was decked out in their ten-gallon hats, with brand new pearly snapped shirts and had their stiff new jeans stuffed in the tops of their boots. One of the guests was an old college buddy from the Ivy League school that Fancy Pants had attended back east. After the introductions, the boss informed the boys that he wanted them to get things ready for a little brandin' in the morning.

"Charles is a magazine editor in New York, and Pierre is one of his staff photographers. They're planning to do a feature story on the way we cowboys do things here in Texas."

The boys just rolled their eyes and grinned to themselves about the "we cowboys" stuff and saddled up to gather a little bunch of cows and calves before sundown to get them a little closer to the corrals while the boss and his guests retired to the big house to have a Mint Julep.

The next morning the brandin' got underway, with Pierre snappin' pictures of every thing in sight and Charles with his little leather notepad busy scribbling down notes and askin' some of the dumbest questions you've ever heard. At first, the boys thought it was sort of funny that anyone could be that doggone ignorant, but an hour or so of that kind of stupidity is about all any man in his right mind should have to take, and their patience was beginnin' to wear a little thin.

The real rub came when they turned the first batch of calves back in with the cows, and of course, the Mamas were bawlin' their face off and came running right to their babies like they always do.

"Those cows look awfully dumb," Charles smugly commented with his silly Boston accent. "Just how do they know for sure that's actually their calf? After all, they all LOOK the same."

This was the straw that broke the camel's back for Vic. He's always been a little short on patience anyway, and it was just more than he could take. You should have seen Charles' jaw drop ...

"Now, jus' tell me son ... how many of the neighbor kids did yer mother ever breast feed?" ➤

"Quick! Let's go tell Dolly!
These guys are REALLY confused!"

189

"<u>ALL</u> of them!"

Chapter
Thirty Eight

Gitty-Up Enhancement

$\mathscr{P}$robably one of the reasons a lot of "modern thinkin'" folks have given up on real horsepower and gone to the Japanese manufactured gas-guzzlin' variety is because they never have taken the time to figure out how to get around the little quirks that horses inevitably possess; some good, and some maybe not so good.

Not everyone can do that. It just might be that the rising cost of gasoline could cause some rethinking of these displaced affections.... but I'm not holdin' my breath.

I personally think it's a mental problem. Dealing with an animal that has a mind of its own actually takes a brain. The secret here is to be smarter than the horse. It's obvious to me, being an astute observer of the general public, that not everyone meets that qualification. On the other hand, it's not really too hard to out-think a dumb machine.

For me, pulling on the rope of a doggone motor that won't start has got to be the height of frustration. I have trouble thinkin' down on that level. Now, if a horse isn't doing what you want him to, there's not only a good reason, but there's usually an obvious cure for the situation.

Because he's got a brain, all that's required is to communicate to him what you want done, and then gently explain to him the consequences of non-compliance. Assuming your request isn't beyond his ability, and your communication skills are adequate, positive results are just around the corner.

Back in the old days when the whole world was run by real horsepower and a fella had to use his noggin to outwit his mode of transportation, there were some very ingenious remedies developed to circumvent the obvious behavioral bumps in the road. Of course some folks were a lot better at it than others, and one of the more creative characters is the source of this little story.

Karl was a little bent over German with a fairly pronounced limp. With his bib overalls and long crooked pipe, he really didn't look like that much of a horseman, but that's not the way it turned out. Back when things out in the country were a lot more labor intensive than they are today, there was always a spot where most anyone would fit, and the bigger operations were always searching for help.

A man like Karl, with his obvious physical limitations, would often times start out around the ranch yard as the "chore man," helping with things like the milking and barn cleaning, and that's just what happened in this instance. Some of the hands that had been around the outfit for a while were secretly amused when the boss assigned the new man a balky team of horses.

Jiggs and Molly had been around the yard for a long time and some of the less gifted among the help had them so spoiled they wouldn't pull a thing. They'd figured out they didn't have to. If a load felt a little heavier than they thought was necessary, they just wouldn't budge; and no amount of coaxin', cussin', or the infliction of physical pain would do a lick of good.

They had the "buffalo" on everyone. NOBODY could do anything with Jiggs and Molly. I'm not sure if anyone had ever tried any of that "horse whisperin'" stuff on them, but if so, they were apparently hard of hearing.

Early on his first morning on the job, Karl hitched his team to a stone boat to clean the stalls in the barn. Jiggs and Molly were gentle as kittens and stepped right out with the empty stone boat, and then waited patiently by the barn door for it to be loaded. The rub came when it was time to pull the boat and its freshly loaded aromatic cargo.

Karl may have been a little physically impaired, but he had that old stone boat piled high. The balky team wouldn't even take the slack out of the harness tugs. They already KNEW it was too heavy. ("Any fool should have been able to see that," they thought.)

The other ranch hands watched out of the corners of their eyes to see just how Karl would react to this impossible situation. After a couple of attempts and "Giddy-ups," the new man quietly tied the driving lines back on the upright that was bolted to the front of the stone boat, and calmly went back inside the barn.

He returned a couple of minutes later, carrying something that the others couldn't quite make out from a distance. After petting each of the horses gently down their backs toward their rumps, he slowly pulled the tail out on each horse a little. The boys couldn't tell what he was doing back there, but they did see him stoke up his long crooked pipe. Karl took a few long puffs from the pipe, then taking it in his hand, walked up quietly behind each horse.

The old German then calmly walked back to the stone boat and slowly took down the lines. This time he climbed on top of the load of manure with his old crooked pipe clenched tightly between his teeth, and bracing himself against the inevitable jerk, spoke quietly to the team.

Away they went. Actually the first few feet were quite a little faster than was necessary, but pull they did. What in the world was the secret to getting Jiggs and Molly to lean into the harness like that? The other hands couldn't believe what they saw, so asked Karl his secret when he returned.

"Vell, I sheen dis kinda schtuff before," Karl explained. "I noticed some dynamite fuze in da barn dere, an' so I cut off a little for each of da horses, and schtuck a little hunk of it in dat schpot under dere tail vere da poop comes out, an' lit 'er up. Den I got aholdt of da lines and ven da fuze was yust about burnt up I yust saidt, "Giddy-up." I don' even have to say dat anymore. I yust make a soundt like, "sssssssssszzzzzzzzffffftttt," and avay dey go."

Try THAT one on your four-wheeler when she won't start.

Chapter Thirty Nine

Horace Raty's Hoot Gibson Hat

*L*ike most young cowboys, I just had to take a crack at rodeoin'. I remember exactly the time I decided that riding buckin' horses was something I'd like to try. It was in the mid-fifties someplace and my grandparents had taken me to the big "Chuck Wagon Days" doin's out west of Harlem, Montana.

That was quite a deal for a lot of years, with chuck wagon and chariot races as well as a big two day rodeo. Unfortunately, their regular June date got rained out several years. That just added insult to injury, and after a while, the poor old Saddle Club volunteers finally wore out, and they just gave 'er up.

What a shame. There was a nice arena built at the Saddle Club grounds on the wide Thirty Mile Creek bottom, and the audience sat up on a north facing hill side with the sun to their backs to watch the action.

195

My Grandad was a workhorse man ... not a buckin' horse rider, and after an unusually rank bronc had thrown his cowboy about halfway to the clouds and the pour ol' boy had finally landed in a heap in the arena dirt, this is what he had to say:

"How would you like to try that sometime?" His challenge boomed through the creek bottom.

"I KNOW I could do it better than that guy did!"

"Aw, I doubt it," he laughed.

Although I was only 10 years old, that challenge stuck with me, and I was determined to prove to the entire world (myself and Grandad included) that I COULD ride buckin' horses. To be perfectly honest, I have more memories of payin' entry fees than I do of the short line at the payout window. But then, life really isn't all about winning every rodeo, but more about gettin' on ever' chance you get and then doing the best you can.

There's a lot of cowboy philosophy in a line that South Dakota cowboy Kyle Evans wrote. "I'd rather have ten seconds in the saddle than a lifetime of watchin' from the stands." That seems to me to be a pretty good way to approach life

In the late fifties and early sixties, Horace Raty produced a lot of the small town rodeos here in the northern Montana country. Horace was an old school cowboy. They're mostly gone now ... or else too dang old to do much.

Now, Horace always had a bunch of horses around anyway, so producing rodeos was just a natural for him. It sure beat farmin' ... at least as far as he was concerned. His father-in-law tried to get him interested in farming once, but as soon as the barley started getting tall and green, Horace just couldn't stand the prosperity, so he turned some horses into it to graze it down. (And you thought you had trouble with YOUR son-in-law.)

The move to Montana came after a little incident in Idaho that didn't turn out too good. Horace and a partner of his had a booming business breakin' horses and selling them to the government. Things were going great for a while until Uncle Sam found out that the horses the government was paying for were technically government horses to start with. (Sometimes horse buyers can be so narrow-minded ...)

Horace Raty

I'm sure it was all just some sort of misunderstanding, but the warrant for their arrest convinced the two cowboys that maybe it was time to pull up stakes and try their luck someplace else, and Horace wound up smack in the middle of Montana ... down around Square Butte someplace.

One of his trademarks (at least in the early years), was his tall crowned Hoot Gibson hat. For you wet-behind-the-ears folks, Hoot Gibson was a famous old Hollywood cowboy actor in the days of yesteryear, and his hat was bigger and taller than anything else around.

197

Horace was also sort of famous for getting a snoot full of hooch and coming home a little loop-legged on occasion; much to his dear little wife Olive's dismay. Well, things sort of came to a head one day. Horace and his old travelin' partner, Ford Gardiner, went out on a big toot and as they staggered back into the yard, Horace saw Olive pull the curtains back and peek through the kitchen window.

"Let's jush play a liddle trick on Olive," Horace grinned slyly at his ol' pard. "You 'n me can jush trade hats an' you can go in first." (Did I mention that Horace was also quite a horse trader?)

That sounded like great fun to Ford. Apparently, the alcoholic haze had dimmed his logic some, or else he had just seriously underestimated the kink in the tail of the little lady behind the door. You'd really think a guy would be smarter than that. With Horace's trademark Hoot Gibson hat pulled down low on his eyes, Ford opened the door and stepped into the kitchen. I'm not sure if he even saw the stove poker coming.

Olive had her can full of drunken cowboys, and she nailed the imposter right between the ears with all the brute force she could muster. When Horace finally stumbled over his unconscious friend, he found Olive slumped in a kitchen chair in tears with the stove poker still gripped firmly in her trembling hand.

Oh no, she wasn't crying because she'd cold-cocked Ford ... she figured he had it comin'. She was just broken hearted because she didn't have enough steam left to take out Horace, too. 🪶

Chapter

Forty

Recyclin' Country Style

Country folks work way too hard and get paid less than minimum wage. So ... what else is new? That's the way she's been for a long time now. Not having enough money to go around and being two weeks behind on your work is just par for the course, but what got to gravelin' Mike and Betty was all those guys running up and down the road, burnin' gas and havin' a ball, with no visible means of support. That's just not fair.

It was back in the early sixties, and they were desperately trying to make a go of it on a little place of their own, but they were starting to wear their tired old bodies out. It was clear that burnout was just around the corner. As luck would have it, those slide-in campers were a brand new deal and "Iron Mike" suddenly saw the light.

"Doggone it Mama, if everyone else has time to run all over the place and not work 24 hours a day, we should be able to figure out how to take a little time off, too. I think we ought to get us a camper for the pickup and start spendin' a few weekends in the mountains with the kids," Mike announced one morning at breakfast. "There's more to life than just workin' all the time."

Well, Betty and the kids were all for it. Something besides work looked great to them, too. That very afternoon they made a trip into town to check out the new campers.

"Hey, look Dad!" one of the girls yelped in glee, "there's even a little bathroom in here!"

They had a great time looking at everything on the dealer's lot, but they really didn't have that many choices. With a family of four girls, they had to spring for the biggest extended model on the lot. The salesman assured them that their three-quarter ton farm pickup should handle it just fine. (They stole the money out of their operating budget at the bank ... don't tell the banker.)

The very next day they took the old pickup back into town and slid in their brand new camper. What a day that was! The girls were all giggling with delight, as Mike got the rundown on how everything worked. That Friday night they loaded 'er up with groceries and fishin' poles and headed for the mountains.

It was sure good to relax for a change, and by the time they headed back home on Sunday evening, they were ready to tie into the haying like they really meant it. There was only one itty-bitty problem. With four girls besides Mom and Dad, the waste water tank was way too small, and by Sunday it was full. It wasn't a REAL big deal, but five girls and no toilet isn't exactly an ideal situation.

"Iron Mike" to the rescue. There's one good thing about being out on your own and having to figure things out for yourself; it tends to make a guy resourceful. The old Ford had two gas tanks and one at a time is all a fella needs anyway, so Mike just drained the right hand tank he rarely used, cut a hole in the top, and ran a hose into it from the waste water tank. They had double capacity in a couple of hours.

Next Friday evenin' found them bouncing down the road to the mountains again, and it was another perfect weekend. They couldn't figure out why they'd waited so long to take a little time off. That extra waste water tank worked like a dream.

It was nearly ten o'clock on Sunday evening when they finally rolled into their driveway. They were exhausted, but it was a "good tired." They were ready for another week of haying. Being too tired to unload the camper, everyone just hit the sack.

Early the next morning, when Mike headed outside to drain the waste water tanks and bring the camper back up to the house for the girls to unload, he found the strangest thing. There it was! The answer to how those freeloaders with no job could afford to spend all that time just drivin' up and down the road.

Hidden away on the far side of the pickup, beyond the view of any prying eyes from the house, was a gas can with a hose running into the ex-fuel tank. Apparently someone had left in quite a hurry after suckin' on the siphon hose didn't produce the familiar taste he'd expected. But ... before the would-be thief left, he was kind enough to leave his ex-supper next to the empty gas can.

Yes, Virginia, there really IS justice, and in this particular case the punishment certainly fit the crime. Besides ... recyclin' saves money ... doesn't it?

Ed Solomon
The Crybaby Cowboy

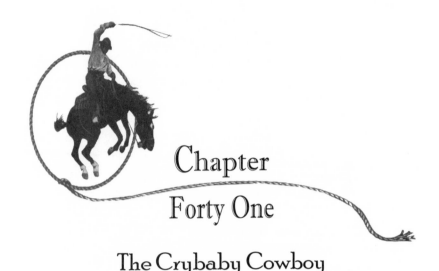

Chapter Forty One

The Crybaby Cowboy

A fella could travel around in a mighty big circle from Ed Solomon's hometown of Havre, Montana, and it would be pretty difficult to find anyone that has even casually followed the sport of rodeo that didn't know him. Ed's reputation as a cowboy, first rate horse hand, and one of rodeo's world class pickup men is legendary.

That ol' boy's from the old school, that's for sure ... a ranch raised cowboy's cowboy. He grew up in the saddle, and was punchin' cows before he really had walkin' and talkin' mastered. (I'm not sure he ever did figure out those last two little details.)

If he's not just about the toughest hand I've ever known, then I'm not too sure who would get that designation. How many cowboys have you ever seen not only mounted and pickin' up at a rodeo with a full body cast and a busted neck, but doin' a heck of a job of it?

The rodeo cowboys of today are without a doubt some of the best athletes in the world, but most of them didn't have the opportunity to learn to be a hand the way that Ed did. There are lots of guys that call themselves cowboys that couldn't even drag his saddle to the barn.

Ed is also a humble man. Even seeing his name in print here will probably make him shudder, and in true cowboy fashion, he really does his best to keep a low profile and not call attention to himself. It's a dang good thing he's good natured too, or he would have killed me for the stories I've already told on him. To hear him tell it, he's still learnin' this cowboy stuff, but with his birthdays knockin' right up there close to 80 like they are, you'd think he'd just about have it figured out by now.

One of his earliest heroes in life, the one that taught him to rope and ride and helped to give him the grit and try that he's had all these years might surprise you. It was his Grandma Redwing. I doubt if you'll find many top hands that will attribute their cowboy attitude and try to one of their Grandma's, but Hilda Redwing has certainly led the generations that have followed her with a measure of grit that most of them just wished they had.

"My Grandma Redwing was twice the hand I ever thought about bein'," I've heard Ed say on more than one occasion.

1904   1964

Hilda Redwing

She was born Hilda Ryan, the daughter of ranchers Jack and Delia Ryan. Although she was a small woman in stature, her reputation as a cowgirl is still casting a long shadow on the north side of the Bear Paw Mountains where she lived her entire life. She and Ed Redwing were married in 1904 and ranched on Bull Hook Creek.

"She always wore her hair tied in a bun on the back of her head, and many times I've seen the bobby pins flying out of her hair when a horse would buck with her," Ed commented.

A horse that would buck was just considered a challenge by feisty little Grandma Redwing. At an age when grandchildren begin gathering around your knees, most ladies begin to slow down some ... not so with Hilda. It just couldn't seem to get too wild or wooly for her. Most gals her age would have been a lot more content with a couple of knitting needles, but she saw an unruly and "unride-able" bronc as just another challenge.

On many occasions her grandkids can remember Grandma getting bucked off an ornery jughead several times while out gathering cattle. Each time, she'd just climb back on board and give him another try. "Don't you kids say nothin' ... you hear me?? You didn't see nothin'!" (Well, she wouldn't want everyone to know she'd been bucked off ... it was hard on her pride. Besides it makes sellin' the horse harder, too.)

So, you'd think with all of these rough and tumble genetics, that Ed Solomon would have been just naturally tough. Well, I really hate to tell you this, but that's not the case. He got tough, because he HAD to be tough ... or Grandma would have killed him.

A lot of folks don't know that Ed was almost single-handedly responsible for the successful trailing of a herd of freshly weaned calves to town to the stockyards at the ripe old age of 4. Here's the story:

The Redwings had just cut the calves off the cows, locked the Mama's in the corral, and took off trailing the calves down the road to the railroad corrals. Although I've heard of several guys doin' this in the past, I've never had the guts to try it. It just looks like a wreck waitin' to happen to me.

But then, it was just another little challenge for Cowboss Grandma Redwing. Besides she had some pretty good help, among which was a budding young cowboy; her grandson Ed Solomon. He should be good help by now, after all he WAS 4 years old.

Ed was mounted on a sorrel horse, and at least began the morning with full intentions of making a hand that his Grandma would be proud of. The details of the horse and the morning are a little obscured by time. I don't know if he got cold, or maybe his feelings got a little hurt when Grandma hollered at him about being in the wrong place at the wrong time, but Ed got to bawlin'.

I really hate to blow his cover like this ... I know most folks think he's bullet proof, but his career as a successful top hand really began that day ... as a crybaby. Grandma didn't have much patience for crybabies, and the louder he bawled the worse things got. Those calves were a lot like chasin' chickens ... they were going everywhere but the right way ... that is UNTIL they heard our little 4 year old hero bawlin' his face off.

Apparently his young baritone bawl sounded just like their mama's voice and he couldn't chase them anyplace. They started following him ... bawling as loud as he was ... (almost.)

That's when Grandma Redwing put her vast experience on the range to use. She knew it wasn't any use to holler at Ed

Chapter Forty Two

Charlie Russell's New Sheepskin

*Y*ou're not gonna believe this ... but Dick and Billy have plumb quit drinkin'. I couldn't hardly believe it either, but I guess it's true. They're those two old bachelors that have that tough luck outfit down on the edge of the badlands. I really doubt if their sobriety will stick, knowin' them like I do, but then ... who knows? I think those boys were born with a bottle in their hand ... at least there's been one there ever since I can remember.

Here's the story I heard. The boys had just shipped their calves, and that big annual check was finally in their hot little paws. Well, just gettin' those critters off the place would be plenty reason enough for those guys to celebrate all by itself, but this year with the price bein' up so good, they decided to go on into town and "Paint 'er Red" ... BEFORE they paid the fuel bill.

"Ain't gonna be nuthin' left when we get that durn thing paid off. We better go NOW," Billy grumbled.

"Just thinkin' about the price o' fuel is enough t' drive a man t' drink." His frown suddenly turned into a big dumb grin at the very thought of it all.

The boys got all showered and shaved up and headed their old rattle trap pickup down the road towards Great Falls. There was a horse sale in town, and if that ain't a reason to go to town.... what is?

Boy, there were some nice colts at the sale, but they managed to restrain themselves somehow. A cowboy with a fresh calf check can get plum reckless at a horse sale. No sir, they didn't buy a thing.

"Doggone it, Billy," Dick said slyly to his ol' pardner, "all o' this horse sale dust can sure make a feller's throat dry."

"Danged if it won't," his pal grinned. Downtown they went.

"Lookey there," Billy motioned towards a bronze statue beside the street. "If it ain't ol' Charlie Russell and that ol' cow pony of his ... "Monte," ain't that his name? That doggone statue looks jus' like 'im, don't it?"

"How the heck would you know?" Dick snorted. "You wasn't even weaned when ol' Charlie croaked." They both had a good chuckle.

"'Cause I seen his picture in a book, that's why ... I'm tellin' ya it looks jus' like 'im."

Into a local establishment with a gen-u-ine brass rail for their boots and a sure-nuff brass spittoon for their snoose the two bedraggled knights of the plains marched. It was about mid afternoon, and the boys spent the next four or five hours trying their best to get the taste of that horse sale dust out of their mouths.

After a while the conversation eventually turned back to Charlie and Monte.

"Boy, I wisht I'd o' knowed ol' Charlie."

"Yea, me too."

"From what I read about 'im, he's just our kinda fella."

"Yup. It jus' don't seem right to let a pal like that stand out in the cold. They should o' set that statue in a buildin' er somethin'. Jus' seems plain ol' disrespectful to me."

The longer the boys visited the fonder their thoughts of Charlie became until they decided to go back outside and take another look. By this stage of the evenin' their normally slow thought processes were nearly at a standstill, and motivating the difficult terrain (things like doors and curbs) was becoming increasingly difficult. Somehow they managed to make the trip.

There was 'ol Charlie and his faithful steed Monte bathed in the cool glow of a streetlight. A brisk north wind was howlin' and a fall snowstorm was blowing in. It was right chilly outside.

"I'm tellin' ya it ain't right to leave a good ol' boy like that outside. Let's jus' take 'im back in with us. Dang it's cold out here."

Apparently Charlie must be bolted down pretty good, because they didn't have any luck at all trying to move him or Monte either one. Totally exhausted from pullin' and tuggin' on that immoveable statue for a few minutes, the boys sat down at Charlie's feet to rest. That's when one of them got the bright idea.

"Dang it.... least we can do is loan an old pard a coat." With that, one of the boys staggered down the street to retrieve an old sheepskin coat from behind the seat of their pickup. They loosely draped it around Charlie's shoulders, and convinced they'd truly helped an old Pard stuck out in a storm, they tripped a couple of crooked trails through the freshly falling snow back into the warmth of the joint with the gen-u-ine brass rail.

The proprietor of the joint knew Dick and Billy pretty well, and when they finally fell asleep in a back booth, he just left them there 'til morning. Daylight the next day saw the bar man back on the job, and the boys now sort of awake, but still not feeling much pain. He treated them to their usual bottled "Breakfast of Champions" and then sent them on their way.

A warm Chinook wind was gently blowing and the sun was shinnin' as the boys stumbled outside and into the early morning street. There stood Charlie Russell and Monte right across the way just like before, but this time bathed in the warm early morning sun. That's when the boys remembered draping the sheepskin around his shoulders the night before.

It was the next course of events that made the boys plumb swear off drinkin'. When they went over to retrieve the coat they were met with a couple of big surprises. Ol' Charlie's bronze arms were run through the sleeves, and they had to use a pocket knife to get it back off. As they pulled that old sheepskin off his last arm, something happened that may have changed their lives and put them on the tee-totalin' trail forever.

They both swear ... ol' Charlie gave them a wink and a grin and said, "Thanks, Pards ... that shore felt good last night. See ya down the trail."

Now, THAT's enough to make anyone quit drinkin'.

Chapter
Forty Three

Plum Excitin' Puddin'

"*P*lum puddin'? I guess I heard of it a time or two, but can't say as ever tasted it ... don't sound all that good if you ask me," Dick snorted at his ol' pardner. "I ain't all that fond o' plums, any how."

"It ain't even got any plums in it," Billy chuckled over his reading glasses as he dug through the cigar box of treasures he'd recently pulled from an old trunk. "I don't know why in the dickens they even call it that. I jus' remember my Grandma makin' it when I was a kid ... was awful good, too ... best I remember. 'Course keepin' Grandpa out of the brandy was always a challenge."

"Brandy?? On puddin'?? Never heard o' such a thing."

"Yessiree, brandy ... an' I'll be doggoned if here ain't Granny's ol' recipe," Billy grinned, pulling a tattered old paper from the box. "It says right here that she's gotta age at least six weeks. If we're gonna get 'er done by Christmas time, we better get to hoppin'. It's already the first o' October."

That's the way this little tale began last Fall. The sound of any delicacy that contained booze just had to be good in Dick's opinion, and it far out weighed any second thoughts about the taste of plums.

"Sounds like a waste o' good brandy to me, but what the heck ... this IS the season to be jolly." (The boys had both been on the wagon followin' that Charlie Russell incident, but that only lasted a couple of weeks.)

The very next day the boys were rattlin' their old pickup down the gumbo road to town to pick up the makin's for plum puddin' ... just like Grandma used to make. Armed with her old recipe, they strolled into the grocery store with full intentions of getting all they needed.

They ran into a few minor roadblocks along the way. First, Granny didn't have the best handwritin' in the world, and in the second place some of the ingredients just flat weren't available in that little one horse store. The boys were forced to improvise and substitute.

"What in the dickens are sultanas?" Billy inquired of his pal.

"I think they're some kind o' crackers, ain't they?"

After a question or two, the grocery store lady had them strung out in the right direction. They were a special kind of raisins ... unfortunately unavailable anywhere on this side of Kansas City.

"Reg'lar raisins oughta work," Dick grinned. "We can jus' add a little extr' brandy to make up the difference.

Treacle was also a little bit of a problem until they figured out that it was just some sort of molasses.

"Reg'lar molasses oughta work with an extr' glug or two o' brandy," the boys agreed.

Suet was substituted by plain old lard, and currents weren't available either, so grapes would just have to do. They were really a little unsure about what effect the recipe modifications would have, but the fellas were pretty sure that all the changes would probably require a little more of their SPECIAL ingredient.

Before long they were headed back home with all the stuff from the grocery store and 10 half-gallon jugs of the best brandy in town. (A fella wants to make sure he has enough just in case a mouse gets into it ... that used to happen to Granny all the time.) Early the next mornin', right after the chores, they dug out their old tin dishpan and tied into it; trying their best to follow Granny's directions.

"How much is a smidgen?"

"Heck, I dunno. Besides we'll need three smidgens if we're gonna triple the recipe," Dick answered his pardner, taking a long pull on their new brandy stash. "Must be 'bout this much," he added as he dumped in a half a sack or so of brown sugar. "Looks like she could use a little more brandy to me."

Glug, glug, glug.

When they got the gooey mess all mixed up, the boys added another couple of bottles of brandy for good measure and then covered the big metal pan with a dishtowel and stowed the concoction on a block behind the old wood cook stove to ferment until Christmas time.

"Dang that stuff looks awful," Dick chided his friend. "You sure it's s'posed to smell like that?"

"It's gonna be great!" was Billy's reassuring reply. "Jus' like when I was a kid. Now dang it, stay out of that brandy ... we're gonna need it when it's time to finish this deal up."

For the next few weeks, Billy would carefully peak under the dishtowel every morning and add a little extra brandy for good measure. Finally the big day arrived. Christmas was finally here.

215

"Granny always said that if a little '
will do good a lot oughta do wonders."

"OK, this is it Dick. We jus' gotta steam 'er a while today, an' then pour the rest of the brandy on 'er an' light 'er up."

With his pardner being so unsophisticated in the finer arts of chef-ery, Billy had to explain that this was indeed the way it was served, as he poured another bottle of brandy over the warming concoction on the stove.

The hour just seemed to race by, and a mere six pack or two later, it was finally time to serve the plumb pudding ... just like Granny used to make. Billy carefully warmed the remaining two gallons of brandy and poured it over the fermented concoction on the stove.

"Now we jush need to let 'er shoak up a while and then you can light 'er up," Billy hiccupped, his mouth watering as the childhood memories filled his rapidly deteriorating brain.

One more six pack and she was all "shoaked up." Billy manhandled the dishpan to the middle of their old oak table and Dick scratched a wooden match on the seat of his pants to light the pudding.

Exactly how the kitchen looked at the moment of ignition is mere speculation. All that is known for sure is that Dick lost his eyebrows and most of his mustache, and there is now a hole out through the roof of the house ... exactly same size as that wad of stuff that used to be in the dishpan. No one has seen the pudding since.

The boys have an orange irrigation tarp nailed on the roof now to keep the snow out. Because there were no records kept, the exact explosive properties of Granny's plum pudding will probably never be known.

Granny used to say, "If a little will do good a lot ought a do wonders."

Not always, Granny ... not always.

Revenge

If a feller up an' steals yer wife
Not only's the groceries cheaper

But the best way to really get revenge
Is just t' let him keep 'er

Chapter
Forty Four

The Odd-Ball Tracks

*W*e had a couple of pretty fair snow storms in this neck of the woods last winter and it really threw things in a turmoil. The Good Lord knows we can use the moisture, but (of course) we were calvin', so that always makes things a little more interesting.

I think it was Will Rogers that said: "Ever'body is always talkin' about the weather, but nobody ever DOES anything about it." Now, ain't that the truth? Well, that little storm really put a kink in things around here, and was dang near the cause of me sleepin' on the porch.

We got about 15 or 16 inches of that nice fluffy stuff, and just as I was pullin' on my overshoes to go down to water the horse I had in the barn, I heard the dog go plumb ballistic out in the yard.

"There must be a cow out or maybe the bulls rubbed the gate open again," I thought to myself.

When I finally got outside and tried to get the dog to shut up long enough so that I could hear what I was thinkin', I noticed the yearling heifers all had their heads in our direction and were bawlin' through the fence. I couldn't for the life of me see anything out of order ... at least at first, but then I happened to notice the weird tracks in the snow. I couldn't remember ever seeing anything quite like 'em before.

"Must be what the dog was barkin' at," I muttered under my breath.

Here's the strange part. Whatever it was walked right down the path we had tromped in the snow, but with all of the fresh fluffy stuff we'd had that night, I couldn't make out the footprints. I really looked for 'em too, but didn't have any luck. I could see something odd had walked there, but I'll be doggoned if I could tell what kind of critter it was.

The really peculiar deal about the tracks was that the snow was pushed down on each side of the main track about four or five inches deep and a foot or so across. The dog was still goin' nuts, and the heifers were bawlin' their face off, so I was certain we had something peculiar goin' on.

"What kind of a critter made that track I don't know, but it's sure got the whole outfit upset," I thought to myself as I stepped back in the porch for the shotgun.

I pumped a shell in the chamber, and stepped back outside, determined to try and squeeze a shot off at our intruder. I could see that whatever it was had tried to get in the chicken coop, because the tracks went right up to the door. One of the really strange things was that ALL of the tracks were in our old established trails. But then, I guess with the snow bein' knee-deep to a tall Indian, our visitor was just taking the easiest way.

I listened for a second at the chicken coop door, but everything seemed fine in there. The old hens were the ONLY critters on the place that were actin' normal. The heifers were still bawling and the dog was still yappin' and headed down towards the barn on a dead run with the fresh fluffy snow flying in all directions.

I tightened my grip on the old twelve gauge, and kept my thumb on the hammer, cautiously trailing the barking dog down the strange tracks towards the barn.

"What ever it is must still be in there," I thought as the dog squeezed through the half open barn door. "That's the only way out of there ... I got 'im now."

"SICK 'UM JAKE!" I yelled as I leveled the gun at the crack in the door.

Thank God I didn't shoot the "critter" that came out. The guilty party was none other than my dear little cook, and the strange tracks were just her draggin' two five gallon feed buckets through the deep snow with her stubby little legs.

Although I felt a little sheepish about nearly blastin' the best wife I've ever had (so far), my philosophy has always been that the best defense is good offense, so I gave her a bad time about having the whole place stirred up.

Here's how things played out. Actually it really wasn't her fault at all. The heifers were just bawlin' because they were out of hay, and the dog was barkin' and wouldn't shut up because he's senile and deaf as a post. I think he just barks to hear his own head rattle.

In her winter chore clothes, my normally slim-trim little wifey looks sort of like a cross between a sumo wrestler and a Shetland pony on steroids, and she wasn't all that amused at me poking fun at the comical tracks her short little legs and the feed pails had made in the snow.

"My legs aren't THAT short," she snapped.

"Oh, yea," I grinned as I unloaded the gun. "Check out those tracks."

"In fact, they're not short at all ... it's just that the Lord created the earth a little too close to my rear end!"

Chapter
Forty Five

Snarlin' Bob & Crazy Ernie

I really hate those telephone salesmen that call you up right in the middle of your dinner to sell you some dang thing or other, but I'll tell you what, they're not nearly as annoying as the ones that make you run for the phone only to hear, " ... this is a courtesy call from ... blah, blah, blah." I'm not even sure what that little sweetheart on the other end is calling about, but I DO KNOW that I don't give a rip.

Even worse are the ones that make the phone jingle off the wall and just plain aren't there after you've broken your neck to answer it. The only thing I can figure out is it must be some computer nerd - turned salesman on the other end that dials a half a dozen suckers at a time and then the first lucky one to pick up gets to talk to him, while the rest of us are left jilted to rub the sore toe we stubbed running to answer the phone in time. Dang that's aggravatin'.

I yearn for the "good ol' days" when folks actually took the time to drive all the way out to your place to give you a sales pitch for something you didn't need. Avoiding those guys really got to be an art. There are some folks that considered putting the run on a salesman a real challenge and went to great lengths to make it fun.

I just heard about a couple of guys down on the Big Horn that had the art nearly perfected. One of them, we'll call Ernie just for fun, had a plane that he used to check his cows and could land that puppy on a postage stamp just about anyplace he wanted to. His buddy Bob was a rough and ready sort that had been in more wrecks than you could shake a stick at.

One of them had left him with an ugly scar that started in his forehead above his right eye, and traveled south through his eyebrow and across both eyelids and cheek before takin' a left turn and getting all tangled up in his lips. It was a bad one.

The Doc that had stitched him back together must have had more experience with sewing gunny sacks than he did cowboys, because things really didn't fit quite like they did before. When he was stitching above Bob's eye he was makin' sure he had things nice and tight, so that part was pulled way up and his poor old eye wouldn't even shut all the way and he always looked about half surprised.... actually, the right half of his face always looked surprised.

By the time the Doc had gotten down to the lower half of the laceration, he must have been getting a little tired, because the sutures got farther apart the further south you went, and the extra skin that should have let Bob's eye go shut let the right half his mouth droop down in a permanent snarl. I think the Doc should have stuck with gunny sacks.

It really didn't slow ol' Bob down much. He claimed he wasn't all that good lookin' before so a little thing like a ten-inch scar on his face was no big deal. As a matter of fact, he used what most folks would look upon as a handicap to his advantage lots of times. One of the favorite tricks these two jokers had was to use the way Bob looked to put the run on strange salesmen that happened to stray into the sticks and onto the road that went up the creek where they lived.

The first time happened quite by accident. They were having a cup of coffee one mornin' when the dust of an approaching outfit came over the hill. Sure enough ... a salesman. They hatched a plan to have a little fun with the greenhorn peddler while at the same time avoid buying something they didn't need.

Bob ran to the bathroom sink and lathered his mouth up with toothpaste, and left a little foam to dribble out the corners of his crooked grin. By the time the unwary salesman entered the kitchen door, Bob was hiding under the table wearing one of those spiked collars usually reserved for a bull dog, with its attached chain tied to one of the table legs.

Both of those boys ought to be in the sales field themselves ... or maybe in the movies. Ernie did all of the talking and convinced the poor visitor he was nutty as a fruit cake. Every so often Bob would come snarlin' out from under the table, foaming at the mouth and hit the end of the chain as the would-be salesman backed toward the door.

"Get back under there!" Ernie would yell at him, "Can't you see I got company?" A stiff kick in the ribs would send "Snarlin' Bob" back under the table while "Crazy Ernie" kept trying to convince their visitor he should stay for dinner. In a couple of seconds out from under the table would charge Bob again,

"Get back under there! Can't you see I got company?"

The guest didn't stay for dinner. As a matter of fact, he barely remembered his hat. He tore out of there in a wild cloud of dust, never hearing the hysterical laughter coming from the kitchen he felt so fortunate to escape.

That dust was still hanging in the morning air as the two clowns and their dog collar jumped in "Crazy Ernie's" plane. Imagine the salesman's horror when he opened the kitchen door on the next ranch up the creek only to find "Slobberin', Snarlin' Bob" pulling at his chain and trying to bite him.

Nobody ever saw that guy again, and putting the run on him was so fun that Bob and Ernie got all the encouragement they needed to put their "crazy act" into gear every chance they got.

Ain't life fun?

226

Chapter
Forty Six

The Long Hard Ride

You've heard about the long hard rides
Of cowboys through the years
Saddled up for months on end
Crackin' lips and frozen ears

Through dust so thick it would hold a horse
Or snow up to your hocks
With a bitin' ol' Blue Norther'
Freezin' on your socks

Now, I never rode up that Texas trail
That was done 'fore I was born
Or struggled 'cross the big divide
In a blindin' winter storm

But trails, I've been down a few
And not all of 'em was smooth
About the terms "long and hard"
I've learned a thing or two

Like what happened to a Pard o' mine
He had the Lord to thank
His pony's heart blowed plum up
Reared backwards o'er a bank

Thirty feet of fallin'
To the murky brine below
What kept the man from drownin'
The Good Lord only knows

Ten seconds in a saddle
Can do a lot of harm
The longest rides I ever took
Was right beside the barn

And the hardest part was near the end
The ground was stiff with freeze
And the longest part... back to the house
On my hands and knees

───────────────

This little poem seems like a good way to let you in on one of the latest misadventures of your favorite one-eyed cowboy. Breakin' colts and grandkids to ride at the same time is not for the faint of heart. It seems there's always one of 'em that needs a little correction.

"Easy fella." (I'm gently purring to the colt with the hump in his back.)

"Rio Dawn! Don't let that knucklehead get away with that! Jerk his head around this way and kick 'im in the belly," I thundered at my six year-old cowgirl. The old pony she was riding had her pretty well figured out and was going the way he wanted to instead of the course planned by "ye olde trailboss" (me).

"Easy boy ... I ain't yellin' at you ... you're doin' just fine ... easy now."

"Faith!" I hollered at my seven-year-old ridin' partner. "Go back and help Rio ... don't just leave her back there!"

"Rio Dawn! I told you to KICK that son-of-a-gun! .... and knock off that bawlin' or I'll come back there and give you somethin' to cry for! Cowgirls gotta be tough!" (My volume increasing with every word.)

"Whoa, Man ... easy now ... you're doin', OK ... easy."

After spending several hours reliving the next few seconds, my retrospection has at long last revealed an interesting fact. This is probably a law of cowboy physics that is more than likely etched on a lonely bunkhouse wall someplace. This is brilliant, so write this down:

"For every decibel increase in volume of the frustrated commands by the party of first part (the cowboy), there is an equal and opposite increase in the degree of hump in the back of the party of the second part (the colt)."

At this juncture in time the "hump degree ratio" of the party of the second part is almost at the point of getting totally out of control.

"Dad blame it, Faith!! ... ," my very last attempted and volume-enhanced sentence was sharply and unceremoniously interrupted by a wild colt squeal and the events of the next few frantic seconds. Here comes another "Long Hard Ride."

229

Oh yea, we finally caught my horse again, and the girls somehow miraculously managed to make a nice relaxing and uneventful little circle.... with absolutely no further instruction on my part.

And ... I'm almost totally healed up. It's only been a couple of days now, and I can already walk again (sort of) ... I'm actually down to only one cane.

It seems only fitting that I should end this little tale just as it began ... with a verse.

After years of hangin' on
Through frozen turds and cactus
You'd think I'd finally learn to ride
After fifty years of practice

"Don't surprise me none he got bucked off, Billy. He couldn't ride 30 years ago."

Chapter
Forty Seven

God Must Be a Cowboy

The 90's were awful droughty in this neck of the woods, but Dick & Billy's hard luck outfit was especially hard hit. The cactus even turned brown. They were almost completely out of grass and the cows were lookin' pretty tough.

"Now, what 'er we gonna do?" Billy wondered to his pardner. "We ain't got 'nuff money to buy any hay ... 'sides it's only the first o' August."

"Looks to me like we'll just have to sell 'um," Dick grumbled fidgeting with his half empty beer can.

"We CAN'T do that! Heck they wouldn't bring nuthin' with the market like it is ... besides we got twice as many mortgaged as we got.... if we sell 'um and the banker figgers that out they're liable to send us to Deer Lodge."

"Free room 'n board looks purty good to me right about now," Dick smirked. "But, there's gotta be a way to hold this outfit together."

From their perch on the front porch the boys looked out across their little kingdom. A dismal scene; complete with a few old ramshackle buildings, a handful of skinny cows, one old pickup up on blocks, and nothin' but brown cactus as far as the eye could see. There wasn't a decent blade of grass for five miles.

It might not have looked like much to anyone else ... but by golly it was theirs, and they were determined to hang on to it.

"I just ain't ready to give 'er all up," Billy chortled as he surveyed their crumbling little empire. He sailed an empty can that had recently contained "Milwaukee's Finest" into the 30-gallon garbage can that stood near the corner of their shack. "That doggone banker may get this whole outfit before this drought is over, but they'll dang-shore have to drag me off the porch."

Just then Dick, (the thinker) had an idea ... "These are desper't times, Billy and we need to take desper't action. The only place I know of that has any grass a'tall is o'l Milton Phillips."

"Milton Phillips!" Billy choked. "That ol' tightwad would never rent us any grass ... 'sides we ain't got any money ... remember?"

"Well," Dick calmly continued, "He's got over 10 thousand acres over there, and he ain't had but about thirty head of cows on it for the last 10 years. Since his ol' lady croaked an' the kids all pulled out ... he's just sort of been coastin'. An' ever' since that horse fell with him last year, he's been pretty crippled up ... hardly even gets out of the house ... the ol' buzzard must be dang near 90. Besides ... I was thinkin' more about borrowin' the grass rather than rentin' it."

"That's stealin', Dick ... an' you know it."

"Well maybe TECHNICALLY it is ... but if y' want t' spit hairs, tellin' the banker we got a hund'rd head o' cows more 'n we got ain't exactly choir boy behavior either. We just gotta do what we gotta do."

"Besides ... ," Dick smugly continued, " ... grass is what them college guys call a renewable resource. Soon as it rains he'll have as much as he had before, an' when she greens up back over here, we can just move 'em back home. He'll never even miss it ... an' bein' crippled up like he is he'll prob'ly never know the difference."

Billy reluctantly went along with the plan. He's got a little more of a conscience than Dick ... but not much. The boys talked the deal all over and calculated just where to let the fence down and put the cows where Milton was the least likely to catch on. The plan was to make the fence look like the bulls had rubbed it down and then just "dummy up" and move their cattle home if they got caught. It worked for several weeks, too.

But meanwhile ... over across the ridge at the Phillips outfit, Milton is bein' forced to look at his hole card, too. He was always a cowboy ... and a dang good one, but at 88 years old the last fall he'd taken was just about more than his worn out old frame would take. He'd finally broken down and called up a store in town and had a four-wheeler delivered.

Lowering himself to ridin' a four-wheeler was a big deal for Milton. After all, farmers rode four-wheelers ... not cowboys. He figured this was more than likely a cardinal sin that was listed right on the front page of the book of cowboy ethics.

"But ... these are des'pert times," he thought to himself, "an' a man's gotta do what he's gotta do." He could barely even get on the four-wheeler, so climbing on a horse was out of the question.

Sure enough, about the second or third day he had his new machine, he took a little ride over to the far side of the ridge. Guess what?? There big as life, was a bunch of Dick 'n Billy's skinny cows grazing contentedly in his field. Milton was astride his new steel steed sitting right in the middle of the hole in the fence, gazing at the tracks, when the two guilty neighbors topped the rise on their horses.

"Mornin' Milt," Dick called, trying to divert attention away from the trespassing cows. "Looks like you got yourself one of those new Japanese quarter horses."

"Yea ... an' looks like we got a little fence to fix," came the answer, never removing his gaze from the tracks.

"Well, I'll be doggoned," Billy chimed in as he stared over Milton's head at the peacefully grazing cows. "Bulls musta tore it down ... it's probably nobody's fault. Looks like an act o' God to me."

Milt didn't say a word. It sort of sounded like a plausible excuse, but then he didn't just fall off a hay rack. He just looked straight at the boys for a minute and then nodded his head back towards the tracks running through the hole in the fence.

"Act o' God, huh?" he questioned fixing his gaze back on the ground. "Well, I'll be doggoned myself. It must be true ... you know that ol' song about "God Must Be A Cowboy" ... 'cause there's horse tracks follerin' them cow tracks right through that hole He made in the fence. ✐

234

Chapter
Forty Eight

Pluckin' Me 'n Lefty

I think maybe all this stuff we've been hearin' about the bird flu is a bunch of baloney. It's getting to the point where a fella just doesn't know what he can believe and what he can't. I'm not really sure we're gettin' the straight dope on this deal.

I've had over 10 years of experience with this stuff (at least I THINK that's what it is), and it's NEVER proven to be fatal ... even to birds. As far as it being transferred to humans is concerned, I think that's all hogwash, too. If anyone should have caught it by now it would have been me. Let me tell you how I've arrived at my opinion, and then you can make up your own mind.

It all started way back in 1995. Lefty Malone and I somehow wound up in a poker game with some Hutterite buddies of ours. Those guys are pretty crafty. They didn't have their cash-stash with them, so to make the game move right along, we agreed that me 'n Lefty would use real money, and they'd anti up with geese and turkeys and things like that. (I told you they were crafty.)

To this day, I don't know how they pulled that deal off. Me 'n Lefty were big winners, and left the game with the cab of our pickup plumb stuffed full of geese and turkeys. It wasn't until about 20 miles down the road that we figured out that neither one of us had any money. The pots just seemed to work out that way for some reason. When the Hutterites won a pot it was OUR money, and when we got lucky, all we raked in was another bird or two.

That's how we wound up with Rueben. (I named him after the guy that got most of my money.) He's one fine lookin' turkey. I should have been takin' him to the county fair all of these years. He would have won hands down.

236

That doggone turkey is just as smart as the guy I got him from, too. One thing that has always puzzled me about birds; how in the dickens do they hear without any ears? I think ol' Rueben hears just fine, and it's got something to do with that bird flu he gets about three times a year. Here's the scoop:

It was two days before Thanksgiving in 1995 when Rueben first showed the symptoms of that dreaded disease. He was young, fat, and tender and was destined to be the center piece on our table. I headed down to the old shed where he was living with my ax in my hand early that fall morning. I'll be doggoned, but there he was layin' flat on his back out in front of the door.

One leg was sticking straight up as stiff as a board, and the other one was makin' a jerky little kickin' maneuver with those skinny turkey toes of his frantically trying to get a grip on the fresh morning air. One eye was plumb shut and the other one rolled back in his head so far that only the white part was stickin' out. His tongue was hanging out about a foot, with a gooey gob of gobble-slobber stuck on his bottom lip.

I'm sorry that description was so graphic. I didn't mean to ruin your supper, but you really need to know the symptoms of this disease, just in case you run into it yourself. It was obvious he was a gonner, so I grabbed him by that stiff leg of his and packed him back in the brush so the kids wouldn't find him.

"Bird flu," I mumbled under my breath, "and right before Thanksgiving, too."

I'll be doggoned if a couple of days after Thanksgiving, ol' Rueben doesn't show back up again. He looked fit as a fiddle. A stranger would have never known he'd been even a little bit sick; much less nearly dead. It must have been a miracle.... that's the only thing I could figure.

By Christmas time he was looking better than ever, so back down to the turkey shed I went to get him for our dinner. You're probably not going to believe this, but there he was again, flat on his back with the same long list of dyin' symptoms that he had before.

"Musta had a relapse," I thought to myself, and hauled him back into the brush patch again. I'll be doggoned if he didn't show up again a couple of days after Christmas, but this time he limped and slobbered around there until he was dang sure that New Year's was over.

For over 10 years now, it's been the same ol' story. Two days before every holiday Rueben gets the Bird Flu so bad that you'd swear to Goodness that he was croakin', and two days afterwards he's back as good as new.

All of this has left me with more questions than answers:

1. If this IS bird flu, it's definitely not fatal. It only lasts a couple of days, so it dang shore isn't anything to worry about.

2. It's not transferable to humans, or I'd of caught it by now.

3. If Rueben's been fakin' all these years, how does he KNOW when the holidays are coming?

4. How does he hear us talkin' about choppin' his head off if he doesn't have any ears?

This Christmas it's all going to be different. I've been telling him ever since he showed back up here after Thanksgiving, that from now on he doesn't have anything to worry about. I've commuted his sentence, so he doesn't have to try to "catch" any disease this year.

We're going to find out once and for all if he REALLY can hear what's going on. I don't want to hurt his feelin's, so I'm not telling him the real reason. He's so doggone old and tough now that you'd have to use a steak knife to cut the gravy.

Besides ... it'd be a crime to kill a bird that's that sharp. He must of picked up all those smarts from the Colony boys that plucked me 'n Lefty.

Ken Overcast

Ken Overcast is a Montana cowboy ... the real deal. He and his family ranch on Lodge Creek not far from the Canadian border. He's also quite a storyteller as well as being a recording artist and author. Ken has recorded several CDs of cowboy music, with one of his songs, *Montana Lullaby*, being selected to be the "Official Lullaby of the State of Montana" by the Montana Legislature.

This is Ken's third book of stories from the Real West. Ken's other books as well as audio samples of his recordings are available on his Web site.

www.kenovercast.com